Goodheart-Willcox's BUILD-A-COURSE Series

GRAPHIC ARTS

by

FREDERICK D. KAGY

Industrial Arts Department
Illinois State University, Normal

WALTER C. BROWN, Consulting Editor
Supervisor of Industrial Arts
Director of Vocational-Technical Education
Phoenix, Arizona

Books in Build-A-Course Series

Woodworking—Wagner

Drafting—Brown

Electricity—Gerrish

Electronics—Gerrish

Metalworking—Boyd

Art Metals—Siegner

Graphics Arts—Kagy

Power Mechanics—Atteberry

Leathercraft—Zimmerman

Ceramics—Brennan

Plastics—Cope

(Other books in work)

SOUTH HOLLAND, ILLINOIS
THE GOODHEART-WILLCOX CO., Inc.
Publishers

INTRODUCTION

Graphic Arts is a broad field which includes the many activities in in the printing and publishing industries.

The purpose of this course is to help you explore the area of Graphic Arts, as a part of your general education.

It will acquaint you with the basic mechanics of various types of printing, composition fundamentals, and basic "ingredients" of printed pieces.

Automation, computers, new machines and methods are causing changes and advancements in printing. It is more important than ever that a person working in the graphic arts understand the basic processes. With a thorough grounding in the fundamentals he can understand and adapt to the technological changes taking place in the industry.

Graphic Arts...a key tool of business and industry, offers many opportunities to qualified workers for year-round employment, at good wages. Your careful consideration of this important field, when deciding on your future vocation, may be advisable.

Fred Kagy

 122-L

CONTENTS

Fundamentals of
PRINTING PROCESSES

1. Letterpress.
2. Lithography.
3. Intaglio.
4. Silk screen.
5. Electrostatics.

Printing is a means of transferring ink impressions from a press plate to paper, metal or other material. A knowledge of the printing processes is essential to an understanding of the work to be performed by the printing crafts.

In this Unit, we will discuss briefly, the basic principles of five printing processes in use today--Letterpress, Lithography. Intaglio, Silk Screen, and Electrostatics.

LETTERPRESS PRINTING

In letterpress (relief) printing, the letters and designs to be reproduced are raised above the nonprinting areas of the press plate. In using such plates for printing, ink is applied only to the raised areas, by means of inking rollers. The raised surface may be type which has been set by hand or machine, engravings or plates of copper, zinc or other metal,

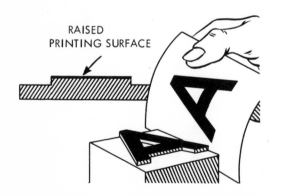

Fig. 1-1. Principle involved in printing by the letter-press or relief process.

wood, rubber, plastic, or a combination of materials. See Fig. 1-1.

The major kinds of letterpresses are:

1. PLATEN PRESS in which paper is fed to a flat surface called a platen. The

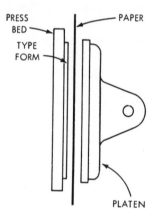

Fig. 1-2. Principle of platen press printing.

platen contacts the inked type form clamped against the bed of the press, Fig. 1-2. The platen press is used extensively in small job printing jobs, and also in school shops.

2. FLAT-BED CYLINDER PRESS in which paper is held on a cylinder by means of grippers and is rolled over the printing form locked on a flat bed, Fig. 1-3. The printing form moves horizontally, and the paper revolves with the cylinder over the form.

3. ROTARY PRESS on which both paper

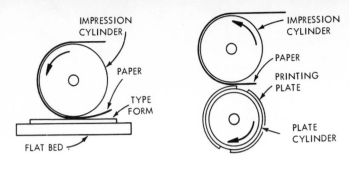
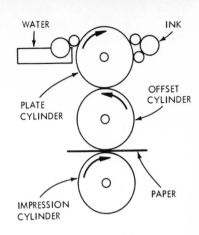

Left. Fig. 1-3. *Principle of flat-bed cylinder press printing.* Center. Fig. 1-4. *Principle of rotary press printing.* Right. Fig. 1-5. *Lithographic (offset) printing.*

and plates are on cylinders rolling against each other, Fig. 1-4. The plates (stereotypes or electrotypes) are curved. Paper used for printing on a rotary press may be in sheets (sheet-fed press) or in rolls (web-fed press).

LITHOGRAPHY (OFFSET) PRINTING

In lithography the press plate used is smooth. Both the printing and nonprinting areas are on the same level, instead of being on different levels as in letterpress printing, described previously.

Lithography is based on the principle that oil (printing ink) and water, will not mix. The plate cylinder is alternately dampened and inked. Water repels ink from the nonprinting areas. The printing areas of the plate take ink from an inking roller.

Ink is transferred from the flat surface of the printing plate to a rubber "blanket" or offset cylinder, which transfers the image to paper on the impression cylinder. See Fig. 1-5. Such printing is called "offset" printing because the image is picked up from a second cylinder onto which it has been offset, instead of from the plate cylinder direct.

Offset printing plates are made from thin grained metal--usually zinc or aluminum, also from plastic and paper.

INTAGLIO (GRAVURE) PRINTING

We learned that in letterpress printing the printing surface or area is raised and in offset the printing area is flat.

Intaglio printing uses a depressed or sunken surface for transferring ink to the paper, Fig. 1-6. A copper plate cylindrical or round in shape is etched with depressions of different depths to hold the ink. Ink is applied to the entire plate, and the surface is then wiped or scraped by a metal blade, leaving ink only in the depressions. In printing, suction is created,

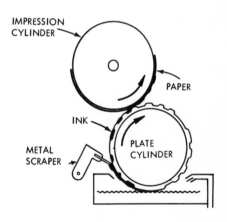

Fig. 1-6. *Intaglio (gravure) printing.*

which lifts the ink out of the plate depressions onto the paper. As with rotary letterpress, gravure presses are made for both sheets (sheet-fed), and rolls (web-fed) of paper. Contact is made from the inked plate directly to the paper.

SILK SCREEN

Screen printing is considerably different from the other three processes we have discussed. In this process the printing medium (ink, paint, etc.) is forced by a

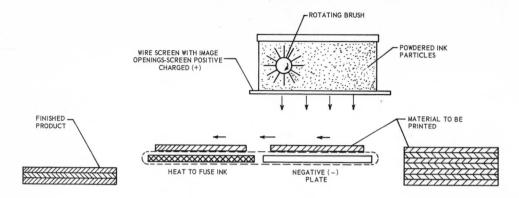

Fig. 1-8. Electrostatic (pressureless) Printing.

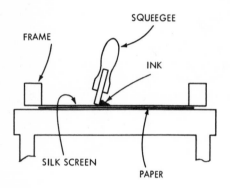

Fig. 1-7. Silk screen printing.

rubber squeegee through the fine mesh of a silk or metal screen stretched over a printing frame, to form a design on the surface being printed, Fig. 1-7. Designs may be silk screened onto paper, metal, wood, and various other surfaces. The design in the screen may be made either by hand, or by photographic methods.

HOW PRINT SHOP WORK IS DIVIDED

Work in a typical print shop is divided into three main divisions: COMPOSING ROOM is the place where the type is set, and assembled into the desired form. The PRESSROOM has presses to print the various jobs. The presses are sometimes of special design and are used for specific jobs. The BINDERY DEPARTMENT has machines to do cutting, folding, gathering and stitching, as required to complete the job being produced.

ELECTROSTATIC (PRESSURELESS) PRINTING

In electrostatic printing, a thin plate is prepared with the design to be transferred to the surface of the material to be printed. The design is open to allow finely powdered, magnetically charged pigment particles to be metered through the image opening to the surface to be printed.

These pigment or ink particles are held in place by electrostatic attraction until they are fused by heat or chemical means.

Since the image forming element or plate need not contact the image receiving surface, materials with uneven surfaces can be printed.

QUIZ – Unit 1

(Write answers on separate sheet of paper. Do not write in this book).

1. Printing may be defined as a _____.
2. In letterpress printing the letters and designs are raised above the non-printing area. True or false?
3. Lithography is based on the principle that _____.
4. What is offset printing?
5. Intaglio printing uses a _____surface for transferring ink to the paper.
6. Draw a sketch which shows the principle involved in silk screen printing.

TYPESETTING FUNDAMENTALS

1. Identifying type parts.
2. Composing equipment.
3. How type is stored.
4. Setting type by hand.
5. Proofing type forms.
6. Correcting errors.

PARTS OF TYPE CHARACTER

The printer's most important tool is type. Names of the parts of a type character are shown in Fig. 2-1. It is important that you learn these names, especially the parts of the printing face, because you will

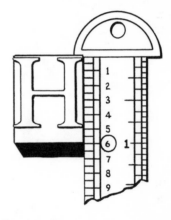

Fig. 2-2. How type size is measured.

elements are called Serifs. Blank space on the non-printing area at the bottom of the face, is the Shoulder.

Grooves across the front of the type are called Nicks. These nicks which differ in number and position on various types, aid in the identification and distribution of the

be dealing with these terms in identifying various type faces.

Fig. 2-1. A piece of type with parts identified.

The feet are the part on which the type stands. Type that is loosely spaced and leans over when printed is called "off its feet." The body of the type supports the face, which is the part that prints. The lighter lines of the face are called Light Elements, the heavier lines Heavy Elements. The crosslines, at the ends of the

type, and serve as a guide to setting the type the right side up. Pin Marks, found on large type, may bear the type size or the trade mark of the foundry that produced it.

POINT SYSTEM OF MEASUREMENT

The standard system of measurement for type, rules, and borders is the Point System. The Point or unit of measurement upon which the system is based, is equal to 1/72 in. The size of type in points is equal to the measurement through the body of the type character from the nick side to the back, Fig. 2-1. The face or printing surface of the type letter does not reach the full point size of the body of the type, Fig. 2-2. Another unit of measurement used by printers is the Pica. A pica is equal to 12 points. There are six picas to one inch. The printer's rule or line gauge, Fig. 2-3, which is used in the print shop, for measuring, is divided on one side into inches

Fig. 2-3. Printer's rule or line gauge.
(H. B. Rouse)

and on the other side into picas (12 points), and half picas (6 points). Type sizes commonly used are 6, 8, 10, 12, 14, 18, 24, 30, 36, 42, 48, 60, and 72 point. Fig. 2-4.

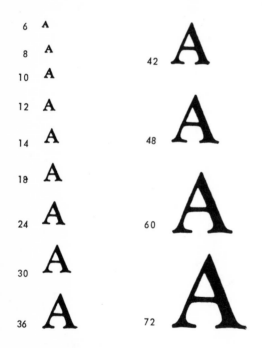

Fig. 2-4. Type sizes (exact) from 6 point to 72 point.

SPACING MATERIAL

In setting type, the term spacing refers to separation of words in a line. Pieces of metal that are shorter than regular type so they will not print and have no characters

on them, called Spaces, are used between words, for indenting paragraphs, and for filling out short lines. Using spaces between the words is necessary in order to make the matter easy to read.

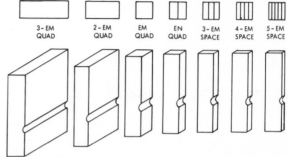

Fig. 2-5. Several sizes of spaces and quads.

The unit of spacing material is the Em which is a piece of type metal which is square, and is the same point size as the type being set. Spaces wider than ems are called Quads. An Em Quad is a spacer which is square. An En Quad is a space half as wide as an Em Quad. See Fig. 2-5. In normal composition a three-em space is used between words.

LEADS AND SLUGS

In setting type the term Leading refers to inserting strips of metal called Leads and Slugs, between the lines of type, Fig. 2-6. The thickness of these strips of metal is given in points (1/72 inch). Leads are 1, 2, 3 and 4 points in thickness. Slugs come 6, 9, and 12 points. Sizes commonly used are 2 point leads and 6 point slugs.

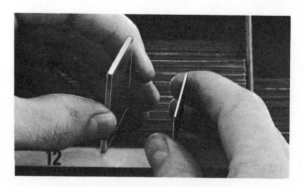

Fig. 2-6. Left, Slug. Right, Lead.

COMPOSING STICK

The Composing Stick or "Stick" as it is sometimes called, Fig. 2-7, is the tool which the printer uses in assembling type letters to form words. There are several

Fig. 2-7. A composing stick.
(H. B. Rouse)

different styles and lengths of composing sticks available.

HOW TYPE IS STORED

Printing by all methods requires the assembling of the letters of the alphabet into words to convey the message of the particular job. Whenever these letters are assembled, some method of storing the characters is necessary. If the process is typing or operating certain composing machines such as the Linotype, Intertype, or Monotype, these machines have keyboards, and by striking the right keys the letters are assembled for casting into type

for printing or in the case of the typewriter, they are printed on paper.

In hand composition, the fundamental or basic process of printing, the individual letters are stored in a shallow drawer called a Type Case. If you will look at the case layout shown in Fig. 2-8, you will see that the section to your right has the capital (caps) letters or characters, and these are arranged in almost alphabetical order. The only two letters out of order being the capital J and U. These letters were added to the alphabet after the other letters.

The lower case or small letters occupy other sections of the case. The compartment sizes vary in the lower case section of the case according to the number or frequency the letters are used in the formation of the words of our language. Note that the letter e has the largest compartment.

A type case having this arrangement with both the capitals and lower case letters contained in the same drawer is called a California Job case, Fig. 2-8. This is the most frequently used style of type case. Should you have to work with one

Fig. 2-8. Arrangement of type in a California job case.

ffi	fl	5 em	4 em	' —	k
j					
	b	c	d	e	
?					
!					
	l	m	n	h	
z					
x				3	
	v	u	t	em sp.	
q					

1	2	3	4	5	6	7	8
						ff	9
i	s		f	g			
						fi	0
o	y	p	w	,	en qd.	em qd.
		;	:	2&3	
a	r	.	-	em qd.	

$	—					
A	B	C	D	E	F	G
H	I	K	L	M	N	O
P	Q	R	S	T	V	W
X	Y	Z	J	U	&	ffl

of the other type case styles, Fig. 2-10, a knowledge of the California Job Case will help you find the letters needed with a minimum of effort.

OTHER CHARACTERS

Besides the letters, other characters necessary to do a printing job are also stored in special sections of the type case. You will find the numbers, 1 through 0, the

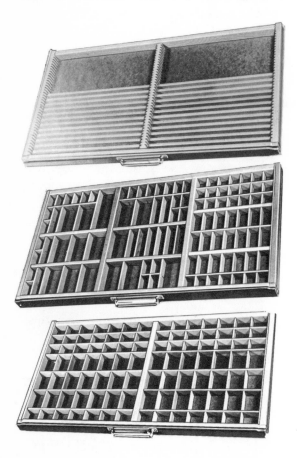

Fig. 2-10. Type cases. Top, Large letter. Center, Italic job. Bottom, News cap.
(Hamilton Mfg. Co.)

punctuation marks, ligatures, spaces and special characters such as the dollar sign ($), ampersand (&) and parentheses ( ).

Ligatures are letter combinations such as ff, fi, ffl, fl, and ffi. These are two

or more letters cast on a single type body connected in such a way as to protect the part of the letter that hangs over the character body. A letter with this over-hang is called a Kerned Letter. The illustration, Fig. 2-11, shows ligatures in a type case, and some examples of kerned letters. Ligatures should ordinarily be used wherever they appear in composition if the style of type you are using includes these characters.

LEARNING WHERE LETTERS ARE LOCATED

In order to set type correctly, you should learn where each character or letter is located in the case so it becomes almost automatic when you reach for the individual letters. When learning the lower case side, you will find it helps a great deal to locate the letters if you will remember the characters in groups. The groups are as follows, bcde, is, fg, lmnho, ypw, ar, tuv, qxz, and jk. The capitals being in alphabetical order are learned very easily. The

Fig. 2-11. Ligatures and kerned letters.

numbers are in numerical order, and are easily remembered.

TYPE DEMONS

As you work with the various letters you will find some very difficult to read. The worst offenders will be b d p and q. These are called the Demons. If you will remember to hold the letter with the nick-up and imagine sliding the long part of the letter (acender or decender) in the opposite direction, the letter will read correctly. This is shown in Fig. 2-12. Two other letters that give trouble are the n and u. The easiest way to remember these two is this: with the nick-up, if it looks like a u, it is an n, and if it looks like an n, it is a u. There are, of course, other characters that will give trouble at first, but you will come up with your own system of distinguishing which letter you are working with.

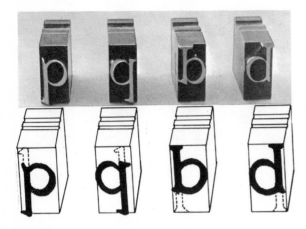

Fig. 2-12. The type demons.

The printer's points, or punctuation marks, can be remembered in groups also.

These are as follows:

1.	2.	3.
period .	comma ,	exclamation !
semicolon ;	apostrophe '	question ?
colon :		
hyphen —		

The other characters is the case are used very seldom and their locations can gradually be memorized.

SETTING TYPE

The man in the shop who sets type is called a Compositor. The work is called Composition.

Before you set type you must decide upon the measure or length of line. In the first assignments, the length of line will be given. As you progress you will choose the line length. It is important that you understand thoroughly, the use of a line gauge, and the printers system of measurement.

ACTIVITY - LEARNING TYPE CASE

Only three letters are used in this assignment, e, a, and t. Set the stick at 15 picas, and use slugs between each of the lines. Use 10 or 12 point type.

Copy

eeeeeeeee

aaaaaaaaaa

tttttttttt

eat eat eat eat eat

PROCEDURE: Set the stick to the measure called for 15 picas. Hold the stick in your left hand at an angle so the type letters will not fall out. Insert a slug the same length of the line being set. Later in setting longer lines, slugs, also leads, may be spliced.

Pick the letters indicated by the copy (10 letter e's) from the proper type case compartment, using the thumb and forefinger of your right hand. Place the letters

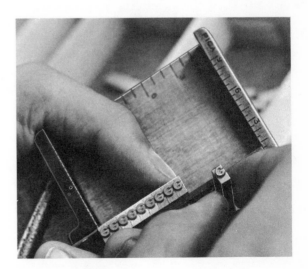

Fig. 2-13. Setting type, first assignment.

in the stick with the nicks up. Start at the left, and work toward the right. See Fig. 2-13.

You can steady or hold the type in the

stick with your left thumb, as you reach for each subsequent letter. The type you set will read from left to right just as you ordinarily read, but it will be upside down and backwards. With a little experience, you will be able to read type in this position. Try reading the type shown in Fig. 2-14.

Fig. 2-14. Try reading this type.

To justify (fill out) the line with the 10 e's, first place as many of the large quads at the end of the line as will fit into the space. It will then be necessary to put in small spaces (next to the type) to make the line of type fit firmly in the stick. If you can push the line forward and it will stand alone, you have justified the line correctly.

Insert a slug, and proceed in the same manner in setting the other three lines of Activity.

HOW TO DUMP THE STICK

When you have completed setting the type for the activity, Fig. 2-15, you are ready to empty the type from the composing stick into a galley (three-sided metal tray). Be sure you have a slug before the

first line, and one after the last line of type.

Grasp the lines of type between the thumbs and the forefingers, and use the

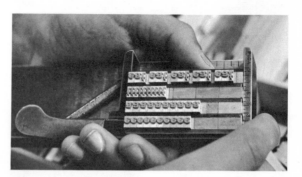

Fig. 2-15. Type for first activity is in place in the composing stick.

third fingers as extensions of the composing stick to hold the type form from falling off the ends of the lines as you slide the type out of the stick, Fig. 2-16.

HOW TO TIE A TYPE FORM

Now that you have completed setting the type for Activity #1 and have the type in the

Fig. 2-16. Type has been transferred from stick to galley, and is ready to be tied with string.

corner of the galley, you are ready to Tie the Form. This will make the type easier to ·handle, prevent it from piing (being spilled and mixed up) and enable you to make a good proof.

Take a piece of string that will go around the type form about four or five times. Tie a knot in one end to keep the string from fraying. Starting in the open corner, wrap the string around the form in a clockwise direction, making sure that the string overlaps the previous wrapping, Fig. 2-17. When you have only a short length left, tuck this down through the wrappings near a corner, leaving a loop below the wrappings and the end of the string above. This is called a printer's knot. The form is now secure in the galley and the next operation is the making of a proof.

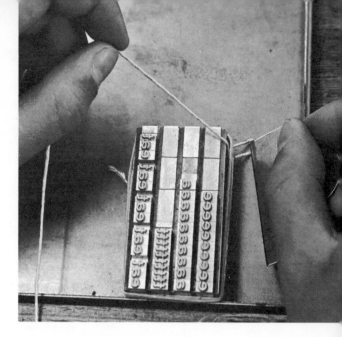

Fig. 2-17. Type has been wrapped with string, tied, and is ready to use in making proof.

MAKE PROOF OF TYPE FORM

No matter how careful you may be in setting type, errors will creep in. Notice in reading a newspaper or a magazine, when you see an error how much it seems to stand out. The public expects perfection from the printer. Let one small error creep into a printed piece and everyone will let him know about it. Remember, even the smallest of mistakes can sometimes change the whole meaning of a job. Each

SAMMY SAFETY Says:

"In working in a school print shop it is important that you, as a student, share in the responsibility of maintaining not only an orderly shop, but a SAFE shop.

Listed here are some points to be remembered. Other safety precautions will be brought to your attention as we proceed with this course:

1. *Ask your teacher to approve all work you plan to do.*
2. *Use good common sense. Horseplay is out!*
3. *Read and pay attention to safety signs placed around the shop---they weren't put there for decoration.*
4. *In working around a printing press, roll up your sleeves and remove your necktie. It is well to wear a shop apron.*
5. *Remember that your mouth is for water and food....not type.*
6. *If you have any reason to believe that a machine is not safe, report the fact to your teacher immediately.*
7. *You should not under any circumstances experiment with a machine or other print shop equipment you do not fully understand. If your fingers or a hand should get in the wrong place...WOW! Even the thought is disturbing.*
8. *Do not talk to a person that is operating a machine. Adjust machine only when power is off.*
9. *Put dirty rags used around the print shop in, NOT near the can provided for the purpose. Keep the can covered.*
10. *Do not use rags saturated with benzine or gasoline near an open flame.*
11. *Wipe up spilled oil. Someone may slip on it, and the someone may be YOU.*
12. *Report any accidents, no matter how minor, to your teacher or safety foreman IMMEDIATELY."*

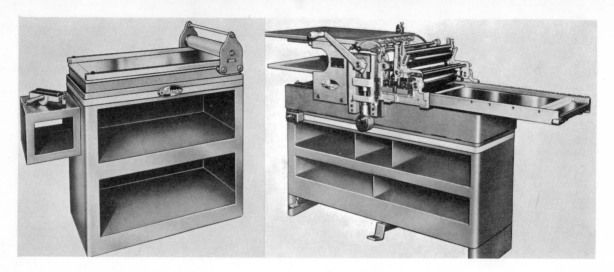

Fig. 2-18. Proof presses. Left, Press such as used in school shops. Right, Production
proof press with automatic inking device.
(Challenge Machinery Co.)

printer is constantly on the alert to find and correct these mistakes.

The best way to find errors is to proof each type form after you have tied it in the galley and read the proof carefully.

There are many different kinds of proof presses. Two types are shown here in Fig. 2-18. One is the type found in many school

Fig. 2-19. Brayer (roller) for inking
type when pulling proof.

shops, the other is the type used in commercial printing and engraving shops where high quality proofs are a necessity. The production model has an automatic inking device.

With the school proof press, the galley with the type form is placed on the bed of the press. Ink is rolled on the form with a small roller device called a Brayer, Fig. 2-19. Ink has been placed on the press ink plate and rolled out with the brayer. This is

where the brayer gets a supply of ink each time a proof is pulled.

When working in a print shop, there will be times when you have a type form locked up for the press and you would like to have

Fig. 2-20. Pulling proof with type form on stone.

a proof but the chase or iron frame the type is held in will not fit into the proof press. In such cases, it is necessary to make a stone proof. The form is placed on a stone or imposing table. Ink the form with the brayer and carefully place a sheet of proofing paper over the form. Be careful not to slide the paper. Take the proof planer (a wood block with a piece of felt stretched over the bottom) and gently place it on the type form, Fig. 2-20. Firmly tap it with a mallet, being careful as you move to another part of the form, not to shift the paper. Continue tapping the planer until the whole form has been covered. Starting at one corner carefully lift the sheet from the type. This will give a proof that is satisfactory for checking.

HOW TO MARK FOR CORRECTIONS

Large shops employ persons that specialize in proofreading and making corrections on the proof so the compositor knows

The type form should be cleaned after taking the proof, so the ink will not dry on the type. To clean the type, you can use type wash or some other suitable solvent. Pour some of the solvent on a rag that is free of buttons and wipe off the ink.

HOW TO CORRECT ERRORS

Take your galley with the clean type back to the bank (working surface of type

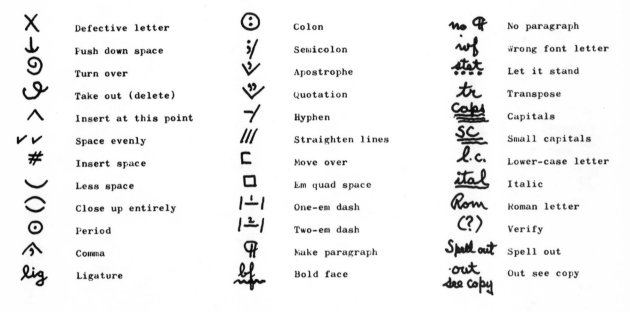

Defective letter	Colon	No paragraph
Push down space	Semicolon	Wrong font letter
Turn over	Apostrophe	Let it stand
Take out (delete)	Quotation	Transpose
Insert at this point	Hyphen	Capitals
Space evenly	Straighten lines	Small capitals
Insert space	Move over	Lower-case letter
Less space	Em quad space	Italic
Close up entirely	One-em dash	Roman letter
Period	Two-em dash	Verify
Comma	Make paragraph	Spell out
Ligature	Bold face	Out see copy

Fig. 2-21. Proofreader's marks.

what to do to fix the form. In the school shop, each student corrects his own proof, and then checks with his instructor for a final O.K.

After the proof has been pulled, read your proof and check it against the copy. Use a pencil and mark the proof for corrections using the standard proofreaders marks as shown in Fig. 2-21. Make an imaginary vertical line down through the center of your proof. Put the marks for the left half in the left margin and the marks for the right half in the right margin. Watch spelling, punctuation and word division. When in doubt check with a dictionary or style manual.

cabinet). It is easier to make corrections with the type on a slight slant. Untie the form so that it will be easy to change letters and make corrections.

If the correction does not affect the

SAMMY SAFETY
Says:

"Rags used in cleaning type should be kept in a closed metal container. A rag saturated with a cleaning fluid such as benzine, gasoline, or kerosene catches on fire easily."

length of the type line, such as replacing a broken letter, or turning over an inverted letter, you can do this with the type in the galley. If you find it difficult to pick up the letter you can use tweezers but you must have the type untied. If you use tweezers be careful not to damage the type face.

Should the correction be of such a nature as to change the length of the line, the line requiring correction should be put in the composing stick. Examples of this are a

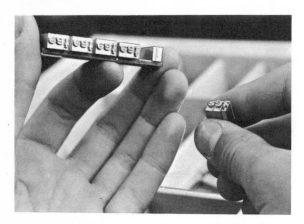

Fig. 2-22. Distributing type back into case.

word left out, a word misspelled, or changing a letter i for a w.

After all corrections are made, be sure to tie the form and take another proof. This is called a Revised Proof.

If the assignment calls for a proof only, you have completed the job. If the job is to be run on the press, the type can be stored in the galley for the next operation.

HOW TO DISTRIBUTE TYPE

While we are discussing the handling of type, we should learn how to correctly put the type back into the case. This operation is called Type Distribution. The type form, in the galley, is taken to the bank where the type case is located. The type should be in the galley nick up, just as you composed it. Untie the form. Take one line of type at a

time and hold it in your left hand between the thumb and second finger. Fig. 2-22, shows the correct way to hold the type. After you have had some experience working with type you will be able to hold several lines in your hand as you distribute the form. Remember the way to keep your case in good order is by careful distribution.

As you hold the line in your left hand with the nick of the type up so you can see

Fig. 2-23. Three styles of print shop materials cabinets. (Hamilton Mfg. Co.)

it, take a word at a time in your right hand and spell it to yourself as you drop the individual letters into their proper compartments. Hold the word between your thumb and first finger, using the second or third finger to help kick off the individual letters. The spaces should also be placed in the galley. After all the type is distributed, sort out the spaces and put them in their proper places.

The leads and slugs from between the lines are also sorted in the galley, and placed in the lead and slug racks.

Be sure that you are putting type into its proper case. This can be checked by looking at the face of the letter with those already in the case, matching the nicks, and making sure it is the same size as the type already in the case.

Now that we have become familiar with some of the basic fundamentals of hand composition let's try setting several small jobs. Hand composition is still a very important part of the printing trade. This is how most printers get started, especially in the smaller shops. The operations practiced here are important to those who may be interested in becoming composing machine operators. For those who do not take up printing, it is our hope that these experiences will enable you to better understand, and appreciate the work of the printer in bringing you your reading material.

ADDITIONAL ACTIVITIES

Each of the activities which follow should be set in type, a proof pulled, the form corrected if necessary, a final proof made, and the type distributed into the type cabinets. See Fig. 2-23. The proof should be pasted on a sheet of paper and handed in as specified by your instructor. On the back of this sheet you should write out the answers to the questions listed with the assignment.

CENTERING LINES OF TYPE

Information

Set your stick at 15 picas. Use slugs between each of the lines. Remember to place a 3-em space between each word. To center a line of type, place equal or paired spaces and quads on each side of the type. Any small spaces that are necessary for justification should be put close to the type so they will not fall out when you dump the stick.

This assignment can be used to make a name tag for your type case.

Copy

Your Name
Kind of Type
Case No.   - Class Hour

Example:

John Jones
10 pt. Century Type
Case No. 11 - Class Hour 9:00

QUIZ #1 - UNIT 2

1. Explain the words: brayer, printer's pi, justification.
2. Where should the small spaces be placed in a line of type when quadding out? Explain why.
3. Explain how to tie a type form.
4. Show by an illustration the relative sizes of the spaces and quads found in the type case.

DEMONS, AND OTHER CONFUSING CHARACTERS

Information

The letters d b p q are difficult to recognize in type and are therefore called demons. Some other letters in the type

Typical commercial print shop composing room.

case are also difficult to identify. These include: I l 1, O o 0, i !, n u, 5 2, and 6 9. These letters and numbers are used in this assignment.

Set your stick for 20 picas. Use leads between the lines.

Copy

> bud dumb quad pedal bump
> drip opaque broad bind equip
> Chicago 11, Illinois
> The phone number is Ontario 6-5290.
> Look! the cow jumped over the moon.
> 555 222 666 999

QUIZ #2 - UNIT 2

1. Explain how to recognize type demons.
2. Name three things to consider in the identification of type to be distributed.
3. Explain how to hold type for distribution, and how to put the letters back in their compartments.

PUNCTUATION MARKS AND LIGATURES

Information

A printer should know where the punctu-ation marks, or printers points, and ligatures are located in the job case. A good printer also knows when the punctuation is correct. Set the following copy at 20 picas. Use leads between the lines. Be sure and center the title line over the type body. The title line can be adjusted for centering after getting the form in the galley.

Copy

> Punctuation Marks & Ligatures
>
> Punctuation marks are called "printers points"
>
> . period , comma ; semi-colon : colon ' apostrophe " quotation marks - hyphen () parentheses ? question ! exclamation ffl ff fi fl ffi
>
> I find my office had an offer but the tariff on the deal was of sufficient influence to muffle it.

QUIZ #3 - UNIT 2

1. What is meant by a kerned letter?
2. What is the purpose of using ligatures?
3. Explain how to make a correction in the type form when you have left out a letter in a word.

LOCKING UP FORMS, OPERATING A JOB PRESS

1. How to lock up a type form.
2. Becoming familiar with the platen press.
3. Press make-ready.
4. Operating platen press.

In this unit we will explore the operations necessary to put a job on the press, and print a number of copies.

HOW TO LOCK UP A TYPE FORM

When the job is ready to go to press it is necessary to lock the form into a chase. A chase is an iron frame that holds the type securely in place while it is on the press.

The form to be printed is placed in a galley, tied up, and placed on the stone table. The stone, or imposing table, is a flat-surfaced table. The form is slid from the galley onto the table, and a chase is placed around the form. With the type still tied, start to place furniture around the form, Fig. 3-1.

Printers furniture is made of both wood and metal. Included as a part of lockup material are the Reglets, (thin wood strips). These are 6, and 12 points in thickness. From a distance they appear to be like leads and slugs. The furniture is kept in furniture racks and stored according to size; 2 picas, 3 picas, 4 picas, 5 picas, 6 picas, 8 picas and 10 picas in width, and from 10 picas to 60 picas in length. See Fig. 3-2. There is also available small furniture and giant furniture. The reglets are stored in racks very much

Fig. 3-2. Wood furniture, and furniture cabinet. (Hamilton Mfg. Co.)

like the furniture and according to length. The 6, 12 point thicknesses are separated in compartments.

For the hand-fed platen press the form should be placed so the sheet of paper to be printed will be fed at about the center of the press. The head or top of the form should

Fig. 3-1. Placing furniture around type form in chase.

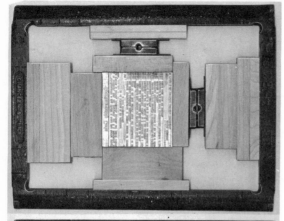

Fig. 3-3. Locked up forms. Above. Chaser type lockup in which furniture touching type form overlaps at corners. Below. Square type lockup.

be located at either the left or the bottom of the chase, as you face it on the stone table. The long part of the chase should be parallel to you as you work with it. The shape of the sheet of paper to be printed determines where the head of the form will be placed. For ease of feeding, the length of the sheet of paper should be parallel with the length of the chase. Now place furniture around the form. Two styles of lockup are shown in Fig. 3-3. The top photo shows the Chaser Method of lockup. Each of the four pieces of furniture touching the type form is longer than the form. When pressure is applied to the furniture by tightening the quoins, (a quoin is a locking device to hold type-tightened with a quoin key) the furniture slides past ends of furniture running in the opposite direction. The bottom photo, Fig. 3-3, shows the Squared Method of lockup. Most printers prefer the Chaser Method.

Note on both lockups: the quoins are at the top and the right, reglets are on each side of quoins to protect the furniture, and the head of the form is to the solid side.

At the top and the right side of the form you should have quoins to hold the type in the chase. The quoins should be located near the type form, but there should always be a piece of furniture between the quoin and the form. Reglets are placed on both sides of the quoins to protect the more expensive furniture. Three styles of quoins, and quoin keys are shown in Fig. 3-4.

When everything is in the chase in order, tighten the quoins just enough so the type

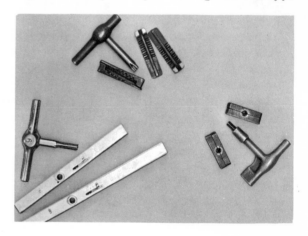

Fig. 3-4. Three styles of quoins, also quoin keys.

is square. Take a planer block (flat wooden block) and place it on top of the type. Tap the block lightly with a mallet, Fig. 3-5. The purpose of this is to make sure the type is squarely on its feet or aligned. Tighten the quoins, place the quoin key under one corner of the chase. Press gently on the type with your fingers to see if the type will stay firmly in the chase, Fig. 3-6. Should any lines of type push down, your type justification was incorrect, and should be corrected so the type will lock securely in the chase. This is called checking the form for lift.

Before going to press you should of course cut the paper you need for the job.

Fig. 3-5. Left, Using planer block to align type. Fig. 3-6.
Right, Checking to see if type form is firmly locked in chase.

This phase of the work is covered in other sections of the book. The use of the paper cutter is described in the section on Binding, page 81. How to figure paper requirements is discussed in the Unit on Printers' Mathematics, page 100.

THE PLATEN PRESS

The platen press is the type of press found in most of the small job shops and the job departments of the larger printing concerns. It is known as the "work horse of the letterpress industry." Most printers have a knowledge of this press because this is the type used in almost all training programs. The principles of form make-up, make-ready, roller adjustment, hand feeding, and other basic printing practices learned while using a hand-fed platen press, will apply to all letterpress equipment. The press gets its name from the flat metal plate (platen) that holds the paper during the impression or printing process. See Figs. 3-7, and 3-8.

HOW PRESS WORKS

When a platen press is operating, ink rollers pass over the ink disk to pick up ink, and then roll over the form to put ink on the type. As this is being done the operator picks up a sheet of paper from the feed table, and places it in the press to be printed. When the press opens up the next time, the operator removes the printed sheet and places another one in the press.

HOW TO PREPARE
PRESS FOR PRINTING

A description of a typical job of preparing a platen press for printing follows: Ink is applied to the lower left-hand corner

Fig. 3-7. Hand-fed power operated platen press.
(Chandler & Price Co.)

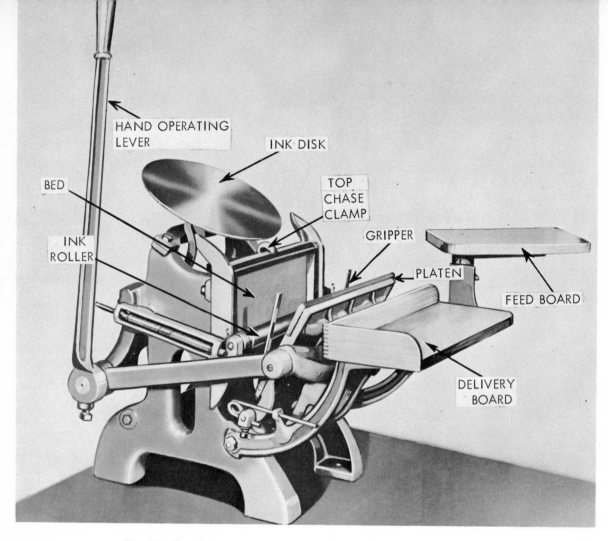

HAND OPERATING LEVER

INK DISK

BED

TOP CHASE CLAMP

GRIPPER

INK ROLLER

PLATEN

FEED BOARD

DELIVERY BOARD

Fig. 3-8. Hand lever-operated platen press with principal press parts identified.
(Chandler & Price Co.)

Fig. 3-9. Inking a platen press.

with the form out of the press, Fig. 3-9, next, the press is turned on, and the ink is distributed evenly over the ink disk. Stop the press with the rollers in the lowest position. The bails (metal clamps that hold the packing on the platen) are then lifted. The platen packing should consist of: a pressboard on the bottom which is loose in the packing, (not under the bails); three hanger sheets of approximately the same thickness and characteristics of 60 lb. s & sc book paper, (a hard-finished paper, sized and super-calendered to a smooth surface) and the oiled manila

tympan sheet (sheet placed between impression surface of press and paper to be printed) which should be secured under the press bails. This whole operation is called "dressing" the platen, Fig. 3-10. When this is completed the form is put in against the

Fig. 3-10. Dressing the press platen.

bed of the press and locked securely with the chase, Fig. 3-11.

BE SURE TO MOVE GRIPPERS

Sight across the grippers (fingers which close against the platen when the press closes for an impression to. hold paper flat against the tympan) and see if they will clear the form. If not, move them back so they will clear the form; otherwise the form will be smashed. The grippers may be re-set after the guides have been placed in the tympan.

Fig. 3-11. Clamping chase in the press.

Fig. 3-12. Making an impression on the tympan sheet, with the power off.

HOW TO SET GAUGE PINS

With the power off, grasp the flywheel and turn the press over slowly by hand. Pull the "throw-off-lever" back toward you, putting the press on impression. This will make a print on the tympan sheet so you can see where to set the press pins, so the form will print in the correct position on the sheets of paper you have cut, Fig. 3-12. If you attempt to make this first impression and find the press feels like you have excessive pressure, decrease the packing. If no impression is visible on the tympan sheet, extra packing will have to be added.

When you can see the visible impression of the type on the tympan sheet, take a sheet of the paper the job is to be printed on and proceed to set the gauge pins.

If the form is to be centered on the sheet of paper, this can be done by setting the edge of the sheet to be printed on the edge of the printed impression on the tympan sheet, Fig. 3-13. Mark on this sheet the amount taken up by the type. Divide the remaining amount by folding the sheet over

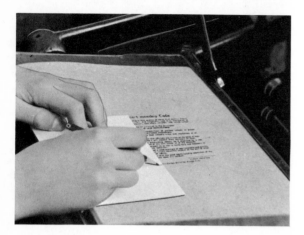

Fig. 3-13. First step in centering the form on the printed sheet--dividing paper between total margin and form.

to the mark. Now place the fold on one edge of the type printed on the tympan sheet. Fig. 3-14. This will give half the margin on one side, and half on the other side. Now mark the tympan sheet for the pins. You can repeat this operation to divide the other margins, Fig. 3-15. It should be noted that you should have two pins on the bottom of the platen, or the long side of the paper to be printed, and one pin on the left side.

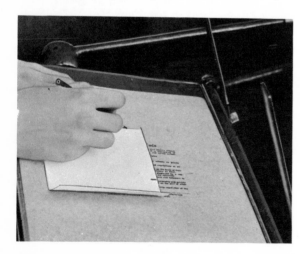

Fig. 3-14. Step two. Margin space is folded in half. Fold is placed on last line of type. Draw line for setting side pin.

If the type does not center on the sheet of paper, the margins must be measured out and then marked for the pins.

The two bottom pins should go about one sixth the distance of the length of the sheet in on each end. The left side pin should go about one third of the sheet width up from the bottom of sheet.

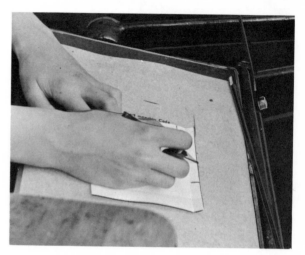

Fig. 3-15. Step three. Repeat for other margin and mark for bottom pins.

To fasten the pins to the packing, they are pushed into the top tympan sheet only, starting the hole about 1/4in. outside the line marking the margin, Fig. 3-16. This

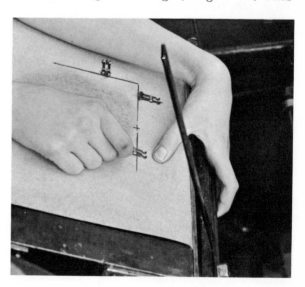

Fig. 3-16. Fastening the pins.

will allow you to make adjustments of the pins without ripping the top sheet. The long sharp end of the pin is pushed into the tympan sheet. Make sure the end comes back out again. This will keep the pin from slipping. The drawing, Fig. 3-17, will help make this point clear in your mind.

With the pins set, wipe the ink from the tympan or draw sheet, using a clean rag

Fig. 3-17. Drawing which shows pin tongue going through tympan sheet.

moistened with solvent. Place one of your sheets to be printed against the pins, or guides, and make a trial impression, Fig. 3-18. If this proof checks out correctly for margins and squareness of print, Fig.

3-19, set the pins by tapping lightly on the front edge with the press wrench, Fig. 3-20.

If the lines of type are not printing squarely, adjust your pins up or down to straighten up the lines and to get the

Fig. 3-19. Checking for proper alignment and margins.

Fig. 3-18. Making trial impression, with the power off.

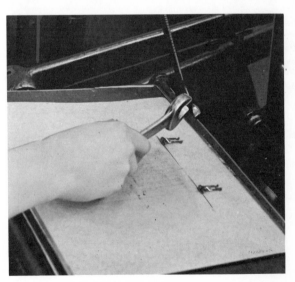

Fig. 3-20. Setting gauge pins.

margins correct. When this has been done, then set the pins.

PRESS MAKE-READY

You will probably notice on the first or

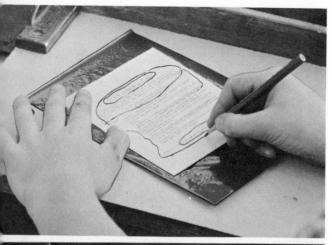

Fig. 3-21. Top, Marking out for make-ready. Fig. 3-22. Center, Pasting up overlay. Fig. 3-23. Bottom, Stabbing overlay for register into the packing.

packing to make all of the form print correctly. Make-ready is necessary because the construction of a platen press is such that it does not exert the same pressure on all parts of the form and there are varying heights of cuts, type, rules, etc.

Place a piece of carbon paper upside down under one of your trial prints. Now draw circles or lines around the areas on the proof that seem to be too light, Fig. 3-21. There are times when a small area within a large area needs special buildup.

Turn the marked-up sheet over and see where the carbon paper markings indicate areas that need additional pressure. Take some make-ready paste, (a special printers' paste) and a sheet of make-ready tissue. Using the paste sparingly, put some on the small inside areas first. Lay a piece of the tissue over the paste, and cut it to conform to the area with a make-ready knife, Fig. 3-22. Proceed to complete the pasting up operation. If you have marked this sheet correctly, this should complete the overlay sheet.

HOW TO HANG IN THE OVERLAY

Place the pasted-up overlay sheet in the press against the guides. Using your make-ready knife, stab the sheet on the right side with a cut like ∧. On the left side do the same thing but make the cut like ⌐, Fig. 3-23. Remove the stabbed sheet and raise the top bail only. On the first or top hanger sheet find your stab marks and paste your make-ready sheet at these marks. The make-ready will then be in register. This is the reason the hanger sheets must be under both bails the same as the tympan sheet. Because you must paste to this top hanger sheet, it is very important that the pins are stuck into the tympan, or draw sheet only, Fig. 3-24.

In order to print on a hard surface, which will prevent wear on the type, take

second proof, or trial impression, that some of the lines and letters do not print as well as others. This is a normal situation. To correct this situation the printer must do an operation called Make-Ready. This is the term used for making the overlay sheet which will be placed in the

the pressboard from the bottom of the packing, and place it between the top draw sheet and the hanger sheet containing the overlay make-ready, Fig. 3-25. Put the tympan sheet down and clamp the bail. You are now ready to make a second trial impression.

If the impression now shows too much punch, remove one of the lower hanger sheets. If the print is still a little light, you may have to add an additional sheet to the packing. This can be added as a loose sheet and does not have to be under the bails.

The grippers are positioned so they will help hold the sheet against the pins, by placing them in the margins where they will not strike the type, Fig. 3-26.

FEEDING THE PRESS

You are now ready to feed the press and start to print. Fan the sheets of paper so you can pick up just one sheet at a time, and place them on the feed board of the press. Set the counter on the press by turning the number wheels all to nine starting from the left, Fig. 3-27. The first impression will trip the numbers to zero and it will start counting the sheets each time the press makes an impression.

Start feeding the press at a slow speed, continue until you develop a rhythm; then you can increase the speed of feeding, see Fig. 3-28. If for any reason you do not want the press to make an impression,

SAMMY SAFETY
Says:

"Remember there must be only one operator at the press. Keep your hands out of the press when it is making the impression. Make sure the grippers are not in the way of the type. . .the form will be smashed. Put all soiled rags in a closed metal container."

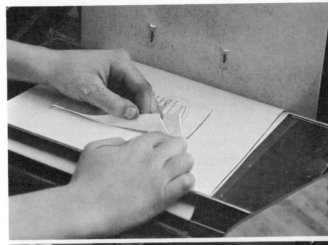

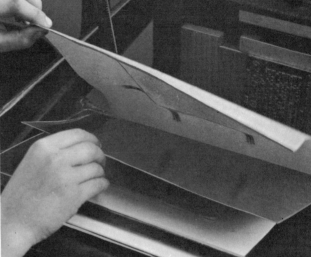

Fig. 3-24. Top, Positioning overlay on the first hanger sheet. Note pins are through tympan sheet only. Fig. 3-25. Center, Placing press board over the overlay to give a hard packing. Fig. 3-26. Bottom, Positioning the grippers. Note the use of a gripper finger.

Fig. 3-27. *Left, Setting the counter on the press.* Fig. 3-28. *Right, Feeding the press.*

move the throw-off-lever forward and the sheet will not be printed.

If you are having trouble picking up the sheets in feeding, put a little glycerin on your fingers. This will make it possible to handle the sheets better.

As you are removing the printed sheets and placing them on the delivery board, be careful not to smear the ink. If this trouble does occur, put a piece of sandpaper over the finger that pulls the sheet away from the guides. A rubber band or piece of string

caught in the rollers. The correct placement of the grippers will solve this problem.

When feeding the press, stand erect at the press. The right hand takes a sheet at a time and places it against the guides when the platen is open. The left hand removes the printed sheet from the guides as the right hand is placing the next sheet in position. See Fig. 3-28. If for any reason you do not wish to make the impression, push the throw-off-lever forward. In this position the press will not make a print.

HOW TO CLEAN THE PRESS

After all the sheets have been printed, it's time to clean the press. The first step in this operation is removing the chase. Clean off the type form and place the chase

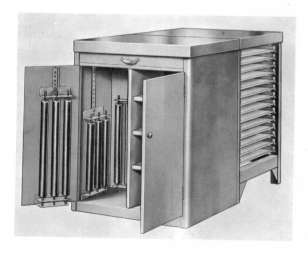

Fig. 3-30. *School-type press room cabinet. Unit includes roller, ink storage; drying rack for printed sheets.* (Hamilton Mfg. Co.)

Fig. 3-29. *Cleaning the press.*

will hold the sandpaper finger in place on your finger. This will help prevent smearing the ink on the printed sheets.

With some jobs the sheets flutter and get

in the chase rack until you can distribute the form.

Moisten a rag with a suitable solvent and clean the ink from the ink disk. By hand, turn the press by rotating the fly-wheel until the rollers are at the lower edge of the ink disk, Fig. 3-29. Clean the ink off the first roller, then slowly turn the press by hand and continue cleaning the

Fig. 3-31. For special operation. In the left hand, a perforating rule. In the right hand, scoring and cutting rules. In the background a numbering machine and a commercial die for die cutting.

other rollers. When all the rollers are clean, clean off the bottom of the ink disk, turn the rollers back to the lowest position and finish cleaning the ink disk.

Be sure to keep the feed and delivery boards clean or you will soil the sheets you are printing.

Store the press with the rollers in their lowest position. This prevents them from flattening as would happen if they were left on the ink disk, or the type form.

When the clean-up work is completed, make sure to put the soiled rags in a closed metal container. This is necessary to prevent fire.

As you learn more about printing, you will find there are a number of special operations you can perform on the equipment that you have in the school shop. See Fig. 3-31.

DOING SPECIAL JOBS ON PLATEN PRESS

Scoring or creasing the paper makes it possible to fold a piece of heavy paper for use as the cover of a booklet. A scoring rule is a special steel rule that is made for this particular purpose. It is rounded on the side that strikes the paper so that it will not cut. This rule comes from the supplier in two-foot lengths and is cut to the size needed. Most jobs are scored with the rollers removed from the press. This prevents the rule from cutting the rollers. Of course, there is no ink on the ink disk.

Perforating is another of the special operations which may be performed on a platen press. The perforating rule is a sharp rule that cuts small elongated slits in the paper so it will tear easily. Perforating can be done at the same time as the printing of the job, or separately as with scoring. When perforating while printing, the rollers are in the press. In this case, be sure to place the form in the press horizontally so the edges do not cut the rollers. Perforating rule also comes in two-foot lengths, and is cut to size.

A common practice in many shops is to save a set of old rollers to use when perforating or scoring while printing.

Die cutting can also be performed on the platen press. This is a process of cutting the paper to desired shapes or cutting slits or corners off the sheet. When cutting to special shapes the printer usually orders a die made by one of the commercial die making concerns. The cutting rule is supplied in two-foot lengths and can be bent into simple shapes with limited equipment. The procedure in locking up a die is similar to locking up a type form. The rollers are removed, and a piece of sheet metal is placed beneath the draw sheet on the platen.

Numbering of tickets and other types of work that require numbers in consecutive order, is done with a special numbering machine. The numbering machine is locked up with the type form. When printing, each time an impression is made, the number advances. This is a delicate piece of equipment, and must be kept clean and well oiled.

The other special operation that we will discuss here is that known as Thermography, or heat printing. The job is printed on the press in the regular manner. Before the ink has dried, a special powder or compound is put on the sheet to cover the printing. The excess powder from the non-printed areas is removed. The sheet is placed over a hot plate or some similar heating device, which causes the powder to fuse. This causes the letters to be raised. The effect is similar to engraved printing. The powders come in several colors. Included are natural, gold, copper, silver, red, blue, and white. Commercially this work is not done by hand but by a special thermographic machine.

We have discussed the fundamentals necessary to lock up a type form, put the job on the press, make-ready, and print several copies.

Each of the activities with this Unit should be completed, as in the previous Unit.

ACTIVITIES

NAME CARD

Information

This will be the first activity to include the operations of paper cutting, lockup and press work.

The copy shown below is only a suggestion. If you have a paper route, or some other business, and you would like to include this information on your card, consult with your instructor.

Plan to print a minimum of 50 copies of this job. See your instructor for the type style and size.

The card size should be 2 in. x 3-1/2 in.

Name
Address
City

QUIZ #1 - UNIT 3

1. When locking up a form, what is the proper position for the quoins?
2. Explain what we are doing when planing a form.
3. Explain how to check a form for "lift."
4. What determines the position of the form in the chase and where should the head of the form be located?

GROCERY LIST

Information

This lesson will give you an opportunity to align two columns in the composing stick. This operation is completed by the use of slugs as justifying gauges. Set your stick for 20 picas. Place a 20 pica slug in the stick and then put a 10 pica slug on the right side. Set the first word flush with the left side of the stick, and justify it against the slug (10 pica slug). Use 10 point or 12 point type. Now pull out the 10 pica slug, set the second word in the line and justify it against the right side of the stick. Repeat this until each line has been set. This same method of multiple justification is used whenever several columns of words or figures must be set in alignment.

Plan for 150 copies of this assignment. The finished copies can then be made into a pad. Instructions for this can be found in the Binding section, page 84.

Copy

Apples	Cake
Bananas	Cheese
Berries	Cleanser
Cabbage	Cocoa
Carrots	Coffee
Celery	Cookies
Grapefruit	Crackers
Lettuce	Eggs
Bread	Milk
Butter	Meat

(Note - you can change as many of these items as you wish)

QUIZ #2 - UNIT 3

1. Why is it important to move the grippers out of the way when preparing the press?
2. Explain the procedure in setting the pins.
3. What does the term make-ready mean?
4. Explain the function of the throw-off-lever.
5. Explain the difference between the chaser and the square method of locking up a form.

PRINTED NAPKIN CORNERS

Information

An interesting project that makes a nice gift for your folks, or friends, are some printed napkins. For this project it is best to use one of the more attractive of the type faces especially if you are spelling out the full names.

A package of 50 napkins or 100 napkins should be sufficient for this assignment.

Consult your instructor about the type styles available.

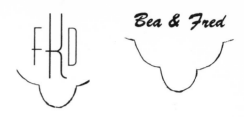

MAILING LABEL

Information

Printer's rules are type-high strips made of both brass and type metal. They are used to print various kinds of lines. Such rules may be used to provide blank space for fill in. They may also be used to print borders around certain jobs. When used as blank lines they must align with the bottom of the letters they are adjacent to.

Plan to print 50 copies on gummed paper.

FROM
GOODHEART — WILLCOX
1322 S. Wabash, Chicago

TO _____

_____

_____

QUIZ #3 - UNIT 3

1. What is the purpose of proofreaders' marks?
2. Give the proof marks for the following errors: smashed letter, push down space, indent an em, uneven spacing.
3. Explain how to stab the overlay sheet into the packing.
4. Give two safety rules to follow when working around a press.
5. Explain multiple justification.
6. What is meant by scoring on the press?

IDENTIFYING TYPE FACES
TYPE SELECTION

1. Basic type styles.

2. Type selection.

3. Printing layouts.

As you work with type, it is important that you learn to identify, by name, the types commonly used.

The first step in learning to identify type faces, is to become familiar with the Basic Type Styles. There are numerous identification systems; the one most commonly used being described here. It is important to point out that the type styles do not always fall neatly into one of the categories, but may overlap into two or more. Most types, however, will fall into these classifications:

1. Oldstyle
2. Modern
3. Transitional
4. Text
5. Square Serif
6. Sans Serif (no serif)
7. Script
8. Decorative

OLDSTYLE

In Oldstyle type, the letters seem informal, as if they were hand drawn. They are designed closely after the lines of the first Roman letters that appeared in print. The form was influenced by the manner in which the letters were originally written, by scribes using reed pens. The serifs are heavy, Fig. 4-1.

Oldstyle is the name of a type style, and does not necessarily mean that the type face was designed a long time ago. New styles of Oldstyle type are still being brought out.

the Best Class

Fig. 4-1. Example of Oldstyle type.

MODERN

Type faces classified as Modern, differ from Oldstyle in that the letters show the influence of mechanical precision. The letters have pronounced contrast between the elements of the various letters. Modern type is a style introduced by an Italian printer, Bodoni, about 1760. An example of Modern type is shown in Fig. 4-2.

THIS TYPE FACE

Fig. 4-2. A Modern type face.

TRANSITIONAL

Transitional type faces are faces that seem to have characteristics of both the Oldstyle and the Modern. Shown in Fig.

ALL SIZES CARR
ied from 6 to 36-Pt.

Fig. 4-3. Transitional type.

4-3, is an example of a transitional or middle-ground face.

TEXT TYPE

Text Type faces, Fig. 4-4, had their origin in the angular letter forms of the medieval scribes. It was this style of

Must Have It

VZ&abcdef:;~'!? 24

ABCDE Fabcdefghi 123

Fig. 4-4. Text type.

letter that Johann Gutenberg chose for his early-letter form. This type of letter is difficult to read and should never be set in all capitals. Text type is used a great deal in church printing.

SQUARE SERIF

In Square Serif letters, Fig. 4-5, the parts of the letter are of the same weight.

ABCDEF abcdefgh

Fig. 4-5. Square serif type.

Serifs are of the same weight as the letters. This face is used extensively for advertising display.

SANS-SERIF

Sans-Serif letters, Fig. 4-6, have no serifs, and there is little or no variance in the weight of the strokes of the letters.

ABCDEFGHIJ klmnop

Fig. 4-6. Sans-serif type.

For years there has been a controversy about the legibility of text matter set in sans-serif type. Most modern compositors agree that such faces are difficult to read in long texts, but have a definite place in setting short material such as headlines,

ABCDEFGHIJ klmnop

Fig. 4-7. Sans-serif type reversed.

and titles. It is also well suited for use where the type is reversed, as in Fig. 4-7.

SCRIPT

Script types are types that imitate or resemble handwriting. Four styles are shown in Fig. 4-8. Script types should not

Modern Alphabets

Advertising Letter,

This Versatile Face

The Trend in Fine Work

Fig. 4-8. Script types.

be set in all capitals, because they are very difficult to read.

DECORATIVE

The Decorative classification is used for type that is designed for special or decorative purposes. There are many different type faces that fit into this classification. Five different styles are shown in Fig. 4-9.

ITALICS

Many of the different type faces have, besides the regular vertical letters, letters that lean to the right, Fig. 4-10. Such type is called Italic type.

HOW TYPE IS PURCHASED

Type is purchased in Fonts. A font contains an assortment of characters of one

ABCDEFGHabcde

DESIGNED ART

LETTER SHADOW

Fig. 4-9. Decorative types.

size and style of one type face. It has more of the letters used often, such as e, t, o, a, and fewer of the letters such as k, x, z.

There are less big letters; 72 points for example, in a font, than small letters, like 8 point.

ABCDEFabcdef

ABCDEFabcde

Fig. 4-10. Types set in italics.

Were we to purchase several fonts of type of different sizes such as 10, 12, 14,

18, 24 points, but all the same face, the term used to identify the purchase would be Series of type.

A collection of the various sizes and styles of one design of type would be called a type Family. An example of a type family is: Goudy Oldstyle, Goudy Bold, Goudy Italic.

TYPE SELECTION

When selecting type for a particular job, three important considerations are:

1. Is the type easy to read? This is called Legibility.

2. Is the type Appropriate for the job at hand?

3. Do the type faces chosen for the job go well together? This is called type Harmony.

TYPE LEGIBILITY

All type is supposed to be read. Yet, because of its unusual design some type faces would score a zero for legibility. A legible face should always be selected. A type face that is ordinarily quite legible can be made difficult to read by the way it is arranged on the page. See Fig. 4-11.

Another consideration is the spacing or

Fig. 4-11. Examples of composition that are difficult to read:

Lines can be too long, as this example proves. The eye tires if it has to travel so far left to right for such long sections of text material.

Lines
of type
should
not be
set so
narrow.

leading between the lines. The longer the line, the more leading is required. In a commercial shop leading is achieved in two ways. Thin strips of lead may be inserted between the lines. There is also an "automatic" method of leading--casting type on larger slugs than indicated by the point size, such as 12-point type cast on a 14-point slug.

Leading should not be confused with letter spacing. This means just what it says, putting spaces between letters. Ordinarily, capital letters may be L E T T E R S P A C E D with good effect in display types, but not lower case letters. Lower case letters tend to be less legible when letter spaced and should not be used this way except in justifying lines of type matter. Even then the letter spacing should not be overdone.

USING TYPE THAT IS APPROPRIATE

In modern commercial shops, when selecting type for a particular job, the choice is so great that it is possible to select a type that is especially appropriate for the job. This applies not only to the product, but also to the message.

For example, in setting a lingerie ad headline we might use *Commercial Script.* Were we to set a headline in a plumbing catalog **BETON EXTRA BOLD** would be much better suited to the job.

If, in printing a speech, we want to emphasize certain words, we could make the words stand out, by using bold face or italics for special emphasis.

TYPE HARMONY

In setting type another consideration is to select type faces that go well together.

The beginner will do well to stick to the same family or families of type, or to set the job using not more than two different styles of type. When different type faces are used, make sure the faces harmonize. Fig. 4-12, shows an Announcement for an Open House, set two different ways. The "before" arrangement shows a hodgepodge arrangement of type faces that do not harmonize. The "after" arrangement is an example of typography

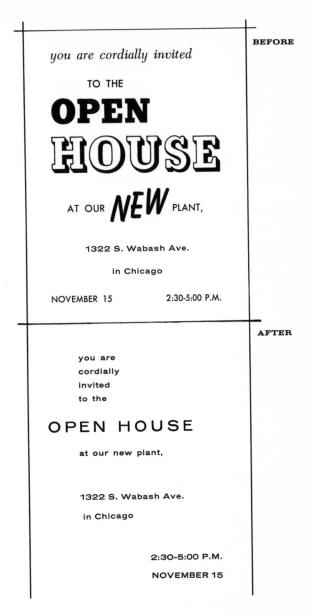

Fig. 4-12. Above. Hodgepodge of type. Below same copy used above, in typography that is more pleasing.

that is more pleasing. Note how the skillful use of white space adds to the attractiveness of the job.

TYPE ORNAMENTS

Type ornaments are small designs cast in type metal, that can be used in composition to add interest to the printed job.

Type ornaments should be used sparingly. When they are used, they should be of appropriate shape and size to harmonize with the type. See Fig. 4-13.

Fig. 4-13. Type ornaments.

PRINTING LAYOUTS

Once upon a time a buyer of printing said to himself, "Why should I waste time making up a layout for this booklet? I'll give the printer the copy and let him figure out how it should be arranged!" That buyer did not "waste" time making up a layout to show the printer exactly what he wanted. But the size of his printing bill staggered him, and the composition he received from his printer was far from what he had in mind.

Not every printing assignment needs a complete layout. But when it comes to printed pieces of importance, a good layout is double insurance--it's insurance against wasted time in production, and against poor design.

MAKING ROUGH SKETCHES

Roughs or thumbnail sketches are fundamental drawings which are made to help decide how a particular job should be designed. These are the sketches from which the final plans for printing, or the layout, will be drawn.

The layout man usually draws these sketches in small size to show the relationship of the main elements of the job, such as: pictures, headings, body of type, trademark, etc. By roughing out several ideas and working over these initial attempts with heavier strokes, the basic elements can be changed and reshaped. Gradually the design takes shape and the layout man is ready to make the final layout. How many roughs are necessary for

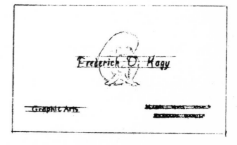

Fig. 4-14. Rough layouts.

any job cannot be determined in advance. Some jobs take only a few and others take several.

When making the roughs, it is advisable to keep them small but in the same proportions as you expect the finished job to take.

The roughs do not have to be works of art, but should be precise and practical. Fig. 4-14 shows roughs worked out for several small jobs.

FINISHED LAYOUTS

The finished layout becomes the working drawing of the compositor. It is to a printer what a blueprint is to a house builder. See Fig. 4-15.

The layout is developed from the roughs or thumbnails. These should have been drawn up after the copy or information was decided upon. The copy should be checked for correct spelling, correct information, correct grammar and punctuation. To save time and money corrections should be made in the copy BEFORE it is set, NOT after. Alterations, other than those required to correct the compositor's mistakes are billed to the customer.

The designer should understand how the printed piece will be used. Decisions will have to be made on the kind of paper, color of paper, color and kind of ink, and the kind of type.

The final layout should be drawn on a sheet of paper larger than the finished job will be printed, so directions can be written in the margins. The main lines of type can be lettered in or traced to look like the type to be used. Illustrations can be roughly represented in the actual size space required for them. Small type used in paragraph form can be represented by lines. The actual copy is usually typed on a

Fig. 4-15. *Left, Rough layouts. Above, Finished layout.*

separate sheet, and keyed to the proper space areas.

Fig. 4-15 shows the roughs and final finished layout for a printed job. When making a layout for a job that requires several pages, a folded sample is provided with the pages and the content is indicated. This is called a dummy.

A sample layout sheet that can be used for your jobs is shown in Fig. 4-16.

Besides a place to make your final layout, and a place for the title of the kind of job you are working on, a section is set aside for you to list the processes necessary to finish the printed piece. Another section has a place for the materials to be used.

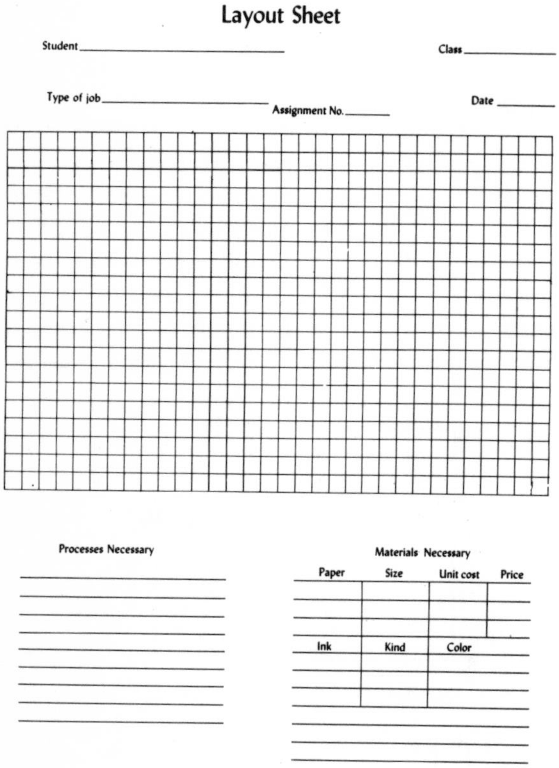
Layout Sheet

Student ____ Class ____

Type of job ____ Assignment No. ____ Date ____

Processes Necessary

Materials Necessary

Paper	Size	Unit cost	Price

Ink	Kind	Color

Fig. 4-16. Layout sheet that may be used in handling jobs in school shop.

HOW TO MARK UP A LAYOUT

In order to complete a plan, or layout, it is necessary to write in the directions for the type to be set, and the illustrations to be used. This process is called markup.

Printing buyers, layout men, and printers use terms, expressed in symbols, to describe type composition so that it can be accurately set to the planner's specifications.

Fig. 4-17 shows a line on a layout with the necessary markings. Let's discuss these markings.

1. Type size

You will recall that type size is measured in points. (a point is approximately 1/72 in.)

2. Type family

This is the name of the specific type family the face specified belongs to. Ask your instructor to show you the type available in your shop.

3. Family branch

This is the particular series of type of the general family.

4. Letter posture

This indicates whether the type is upright (Rom), or is on an angle or italic (It).

5. Composition

This refers to the combination of the letters used.

all capitals ....caps
all lower case.................lc
capitals and lower case ....caps & lc
small caps ....sc
caps and small caps.........caps & sc

6. Use of space

Many lines do not completely fill out the space on the layout so some indication of where the space must go is necessary.

flush left..........................Fl l
flush right.......................Fl R
centered.....................ctr
indented.........................l   l 2 etc.
flush left and right...........Fl l & R

7. Line width

How wide should the composing stick be adjusted to set this job? The figure is expressed in pica width.

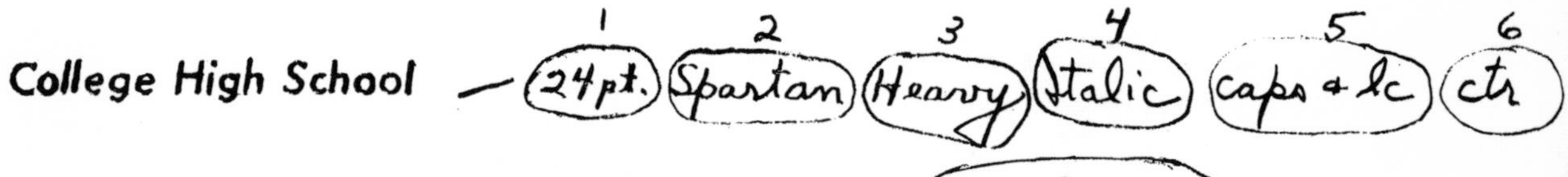

the number of lines the typewritten copy will make.

Now we need to know the depth of the space needed for the copy to be set in type. From tables also supplied by type manufacturers, we can obtain the depth of popular text sizes (information on number of lines of type per inch). By dividing the total number of lines, by the number of lines per inch, we will find out the depth in inches of the space required for the copy.

In layout work and the planning of printing, there are many opportunities for those with some artistic ability that enjoy this kind of work. In the small printing estab-

Fig. 4-17. Line with markings which indicate how the copy is to be set.

COPY FITTING

Before setting typewritten copy, it should be measured to see if it will fit into the available space.

A popular method of measuring typewritten copy is by using the "character count." After the type face to be used has been selected, and the size determined, information on the number of characters that particular type will run per pica is obtained from a character chart (type character charts are supplied by type manufacturers). The typewriten copy is then measured. A vertical line is drawn through the typewritten copy at the average line length. The number of characters in one average line is counted. The figure obtained is multiplied by the number of lines in the copy. This gives us the total number of characters in the copy to be set. Dividing this number by the number of characters in the copy to be used, gives us

lishments, the foreman or the owner usually does this work. In many cases the layout man and planner does not work for a printer, but is employed by an advertising agency, or on the advertising staff of the company buying the printing.

ACTIVITIES

Suggested activities for Unit 4, follow.

If you have in mind additional, or substitute activities you may discuss them with your instructor.

PERSONAL STATIONERY

Information

This job will give you an opportunity to plan your work. Start by making at least four roughs or thumbnails. Choose one you like and make a layout. Markup for composition.

To enhance the beauty of your stationery you may want to use Virkotype powder on the job before the ink dries. Apply the powder then hold the sheet over a hot plate until the powder on the ink fuses. This will make your letterhead look like it has been engraved. The process may also be used in printing envelopes.

Practical work

Make four roughs of ideas for letter-heads and envelopes

Make a finished layout

Mark up for composition

Set type for both letterhead and envelope

Cut stock for 50 copies of letterhead (make size to fit available envelopes)

Lockup and print

Note: When you plan on using the thermographic process, print about 12 copies, then powder and heat. Repeat until desired number of copies are printed.

DIE-CUTTING

Information

An interesting project that will go along with the napkins you printed in a previous job will be some coasters for glasses. This will also add the operation of die-cutting discussed briefly in Unit 3. When die-cutting on a platen press, be sure to take out the rollers and store them so the weight is not on the rollers. Under the tympan sheet you should place a sheet of galvanized iron about the same size as the platen.

Practical work

Make roughs of your ideas
Make finished layout and markup
Cut paper to desired size
  (Use blotter stock as it is absorbent)
Print design on the square cut stock
  (If several colors, a run for each color will be necessary)
Lockup die-cutter, remove rollers, and put galvanized sheet under tympan sheet
Complete the die-cutting

QUIZ #1 - UNIT 4

1. Name six basic type styles.
2. In Oldstyle type the letters seem informal as if they were _____ drawn.
3. Modern type faces are so-called because they are new. True or false?
4. Is text type easy to read, or difficult to read?
5. By what feature may sans-serif type be identified?
6. Script types resemble _____.
7. Do italic types lean to the right, or to the left?
8. How is type purchased?
9. Does a font of type contain the same quantity of each of the letters? Why?

QUIZ #2 - UNIT 4

1. Were we to purchase several fonts of type of different sizes, the term used to identify the purchase would be _____ of type.
2. Name two considerations that are important when selecting type for a particular job.
3. Letter spacing means to put space ____.
4. What is a printing layout?
5. A finished layout should include information on _____.
6. Why is it important to make corrections in the copy before it is set, rather than after?
7. What do these terms used by printers mean: caps   fl l
                                                  lc   ctr
                                                  sc

THE LETTERPRESS INDUSTRY

UNIT 5

1. Machines used to set type.
2. Plates for commercial printing.
3. Equipment used by industry.
4. Making printing plates (linoleum, rubber) in the classroom.

MACHINE-SET COMPOSITION

In commercial print shops using letterpress equipment, hand-set composition is ordinarily used for titles, headlines, and other spots where but few words are required. Most text copy is machine set.

LINOTYPE AND INTERTYPE MACHINES

Typesetting machines most commonly used are the Linotype, Fig. 5-1, and the Intertype, Fig. 5-2. The machines are being discussed together, as they are similar in construction and operation.

Both the Linotype and the Intertype machines cast complete line slugs from matrices. A matrix is a piece of brass or bronze into which the shape of the type character is formed in reverse. As the operator works the keys of the machine, the matrices are dropped by the machine into a mold, and are automatically spaced. A solid slug (piece of type metal) is then cast using molten type metal, which bears a line of raised letters suitable for printing. After casting, the matrices are automatically re-distributed. The type slugs are assembled by hand into type forms ready for printing. After the slugs have served their purpose, the metal is melted and used again.

Figure 5-3, shows a type casting machine which is operated by Teletype tape, and has no keyboard. The original tape may be punched elsewhere, even in a distant

Fig. 5-1. Left. Mergenthaler Linotype 'Elektron' hot metal linecasting machine with tape operation attachment. Fig. 5-2. Center. Intertype slug-casting machine. Fig. 5-3. Right. Intertype Linecasting machine which operates from Teletype tape. Note that this machine has no keyboard.

Fig. 5-4. Left, Monotype keyboard unit. Right, Caster unit.
(Lanston Monotype Co.)

city. News services and newspapers use such equipment extensively.

MONOTYPE

A Monotype machine, Fig. 5-4, consists of two separate units. The keyboard unit, shown at the left, is operated to punch holes in a paper roll. This roll is placed in the caster unit, which casts individual letters. The letters come out of the ma-

chine correctly spaced, and the lines are justified (right hand margins are straight). The individual letters cast by a Monotype are similar in appearance to type used in hand composition. In fact, some shops use Monotype letters for hand setting.

LUDLOW

A Ludlow typecasting machine, Fig. 5-5, is used mostly for casting type used in

Fig. 5-5. Ludlow caster with matrix cases.
(Ludlow Typographic Co.)

advertisements and newspaper headlines. The operator of the machine sets the individual brass molds by hand, in a special composing stick. When the stick is full, he places it in the machine which produces a type slug similar to that produced on a Linotype or Intertype machine, except the large letters are on a small body. Blank slugs must be used to support the overhanging letters. After each line is cast, the brass molds are distributed back in the case, by hand.

MATERIAL CASTERS

Material casters are hot metal machines which make lead, slug, rule, and border material. Such machines have interchangeable molds that can be used to produce a wide variety of borders as well as leads and slugs of different thicknesses.

COLD-TYPE MACHINES

Some information on machines that set type without the use of hot metals, called cold-type machines, will be found in the Unit on Lithography and Offset Printing, page 62.

LETTERPRESS PLATES

PHOTOENGRAVINGS

Up to this time, in our study of graphic arts procedures, we have been concerned mostly with the printing of words. As you know, most printed pieces today include illustrations. In this Unit, we will find out how plates used in printing illustrations, called Photoengravings are made, and how they are used.

LINE ENGRAVINGS

A Line Engraving is a photoengraving used to print illustrations, copy for which is in solid black—lines, crosshatching, dots, stipples, and solid areas and forms. See Figs. 5-6, and 5-7.

The first step in making a line engraving

Fig. 5-6. Left, Drawing which is suitable for reproduction by using a line engraving. Fig. 5-7. Right, Line engraving of illustration shown at left.

is photographic. The original copy is fastened to the copyboard of a camera, such as shown in Fig. 5-8, and is illuminated by powerful lights. The camera is focused to the exact size required in the final reproduction, and a negative is made on photographic film or plate. In the negative; the background area is opaque, and the lines which are to be reproduced are transparent in order to permit light to pass through.

The negative is stripped from its supporting base, and turned over to reverse the image. This is required since the image will again be reversed, in printing on paper. The negative is assembled along

Fig. 5-8. Camera used for photoengraving.
(Lanston Co.)

with other similar negatives on a sheet of heavy plate glass called a "flat."

The flat is placed face down on a metal plate (usually zinc, but copper is sometimes used) which has been coated with a light sensitive solution and allowed to dry. The glass flat and the sensitized metal plate are placed in a machine in which a vacuum is created to insure perfect contact between the glass and metal.

The negative serves as a stencil, per-

mitting light from a powerful arc lamp during the exposure, to pass through the transparent lines. Light affects the light-sensitive coating on the metal plate. After proper exposure, the metal plate is developed. The part of the plate that has been acted upon by the light--lines, solids, etc., is "fixed." The coating is washed off the rest of the plate. The image left on the plate is acid resistant.

Imperfections are corrected with acid-resistant ink, then the plate is ready to be etched with acid. Acid baths, by controlled applications, etch away the background, and leave the protected image in relief. The non-printing portions of the plate are mechanically routed to greater depth, leaving the reproduction in relief.

The completed engraving is then mounted on wood or metal base, trimmed to size, and planed down to the proper height which is .918 in. The line engraving is then proofed on a proof press, and carefully inspected. Weak lines in reverse and other imperfections are corrected by hand engraving.

In preparing copy for line reproduction, the drawing paper or surface should be as white as possible, and a waterproof, dead-black ink, free from any bluish tinge, should be used.

HALFTONE ENGRAVINGS

A halftone engraving is used to reproduce photos, wash drawings, and other illustrations which have variations in tone from light to dark. In printing, a uniform coating of ink is deposited on the paper. The appearance of tones which vary in darkness, is obtained by breaking up the image into small dots which vary in size and shape, but which are equally spaced on the paper. The light tones are reproduced by very small dots, while larger dots are used to reproduce the darker tones. Halftone dots are so small that the eye sees the dots as continuous tones rather than small, individual dots. The halftone dots with their minute printing surfaces, accept ink and transfer it to the paper on the printing press.

HALFTONE SCREEN

In making a halftone engraving a halftone screen is required. This consists of two sheets of clear glass, each having parallel opaque lines ruled and etched on one side, and running diagonally over the surface. The sheets of glass are cemented together with the ruled sides together, and the lines crossing at right angles: In making an engraving the copy is photographed by the camera, through a halftone screen. The opaque crosslines of the screen break up the image into halftone dots.

The number of lines to the inch determines the coarseness of the screen. A 55-line screen for example is a coarse screen having only 55 lines to the inch. A 133-line screen such as is used in making halftones for this book is a fine screen having 133 lines to the inch.

The halftone screen to use in making an engraving depends mostly on the paper to be used for the job. In printing on newsprint a coarse screen of 55 to 85 lines per inch is required to prevent the dots from filling in. Coated letterpress stock will take halftones up to 150 lines per inch. Fig. 5-9, shows a halftone with 55, and 133-line screen areas.

Halftones of 100-line screen and finer are usually etched on copper; those of coarser screen are often etched on zinc or magnesium. The etching process is more complicated than required for making line engravings. Space limitations prevent us from describing the complete step-by-step procedure.

Photos used for making halftones should have sharp, well-defined detail, and tone values, especially in the middle tones and shadows.

PLASTIC PRINTING PLATES

A Dycril printing plate is an original plate with a thin layer of plastic called photoplymer, bonded to a metal support. It can be used as either a direct letterpress plate on conventional equipment, a wrap-around letterpress plate, or an indirect (dry offset) printing plate. The duPont Company makes the plate material which is sold to engravers for processing.

Another plastic printing plate is made by the Kodak Company. This is called the Kodal Relief Plate. It is also plastic bonded to a metal support. It is designed for shallow relief, and is used for wrap-around and dry offset applications.

Fig. 5-9. Halftone screens, 55 screen and 133 screen.

Both Dycril and Kodal plates require a negative of the image to be printed. This negative is then contact printed to the plate material leaving the image exposed on the plate.

The duPont Dycril plate works on the principle of the polymerization of the plastic in the image area. The unexposed sections are then washed away by a caustic soda solution in a special spray cabinet.

The Kodal relief plate has a silver halide emulsion like photographic film. After exposure, this plate is developed in a chemical solution which forms a hardened image. The unexposed areas are then scrubbed away in a special processing machine.

DUPLICATE PRINTING PLATES

Many letterpréss shops do not print with the original engravings but use the originals called "pattern" plates, only as masters for making duplicates. Using duplicates for printing protects the more expensive originals which might be damaged while on the press. This is particularly true in color printing. The plates include not only copies of the original engravings, but of the type as well.

The duplicate plates may be Stereotypes, Electrotypes, or Plastic or Rubber Plates.

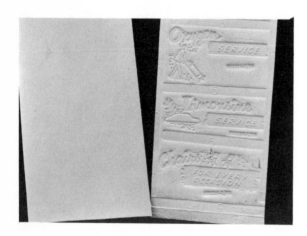

Fig. 5-10. Stereotype mats. Left, Mat stock. Right, Mat which is ready for use.

Brief descriptions of the making of the more commonly used plate duplicates, Stereotypes and Electrotypes, follow.

HOW STEREOTYPES ARE MADE

To make a stereotype, the original engraving and the type are locked-up as for printing. This form is then placed on a molding press with a special papier-mache (mat paper) put over the form. Under heavy pressure, the form and paper are rolled out, leaving the impression of the type and illustrations in the special paper called a matrix, or mat. Fig. 5-10 shows stereotype matrix material before and after forming

Fig. 5-11. Matrix molding press. (Greeley, Colo. Tribune)

in the molding press. A molding press is shown in Fig. 5-11.

The prepared matrix is placed in a casting box, molten type metal is poured into the caster and a stereotype plate is formed. Fig. 5-12 shows a curved cast stereotype. This type of printing plate is used extensively in newspaper work.

Fig. 5–12. Curved stereotype plate. (Greeley, Colo. Tribune)

ELECTROTYPES

An Electrotype is a precision printing plate used for more exacting work than Stereotypes and for color printing.

In making an electrotype, the first process is also making a matrix in a special hydraulic press. The matrix material for the electrotype is a more precision material such as sheet lead, plastic, or a wax. The matrix, after being formed, is made electrically conductive by spraying it with silver, or coating it with graphite. It is then placed in a special tank, and by the electroplating process a shell is formed on the matrix that will become the printing

Fig. 5-13. Left. Electrotype mounted on wood. Right. Curved electro for a rotary press.

face of the new plate. Type metal is used to back up this thin shell and the electrotype is either made type high by mounting on a block, or is prepared for use on a rotary press. Fig. 5-13 shows a wood-mounted, type high electrotype; and one curved for a rotary press.

METALS USED

Lead, tin and antimony are the principal metals used in making alloys for type casting.

Lead alone is too soft to be used in type metal, metallurgists have devised an alloy

which has the characteristics necessary for printing type.

Antimony when added to the lead imparts hardness to the alloy, and increases the fluidity of the molten metal (causes it to flow with less resistance). The lead and antimony together has the fluid characteristic necessary to fill out the mold.

Tin when added to type metal also helps with the fluidity of the alloy. Tin gives body to the alloy, adding to the toughness. It also helps give the metal its smooth appearance, which makes the type print better.

LETTERPRESS PRINTING BY INDUSTRY

We have discussed in previous Units, the Basic Operations Necessary to Print by Letterpress (Unit 1), and the Step-By-Step Procedure of Using a Hand-Fed Platen Type Press (Unit 3).

Letterpresses used by industry are larger and many turn out thousands of printed sections per hour, compared to the few that can be turned out by a hand-fed press, but the fundamental printing processes are the same. All letterpress printing is done from a raised surface.

To give you an idea of the type letterpress printing equipment used by industry, we have included in this book, photos of typical press equipment. See Figs. 5-14, to 5-17 inclusive.

MAKING PRINTING PLATES IN THE CLASSROOM

Because it takes special equipment to perform commercial plate-making operations, and most schools do not have this type equipment, we will describe in this Unit, two plate-making procedures that are practical in the classroom--Linoleum block making, and rubber stamp making.

Fig. 5-14. Letterpresses used by industry. Above, Left, Miehle extravert vertical press. Above, Right, Heidelberg automatic platen press. Below, Left, Harris-Intertype 43 x 60 in., Wrap-Around letterpress. Below, Right, Chandler & Price automatic platen press.

Fig. 5-15. Above, Goss Cox-O-Type press. This is a flat-bed press which works like a cylinder press, but the paper is fed from a roll. Such a press is used by small town newspapers. Fig. 5-16. Center, Goss Unitube rotary press. Fig. 5-17. Below, Goss Headliner press installation at Chicago Sun-Times newspaper.

LINOLEUM BLOCK PRINTING PLATES

In making a linoleum block plate or cut for printing, the only requirements are a type-high linoleum block (.918 inch), and some carving tools, Fig. 5-18.

Linoleum blocks can be purchased already mounted type high, or the linoleum can be obtained and glued onto wood blocks, to bring the printing area up to type high.

DESIGNS

Designs for linoleum block printing must be kept simple. The lines should be heavy, and the illustrations made up of bold masses of black and white. An example of a suitable design is the bookplate, Fig. 5-19. Some additional design suggestions are shown in Fig. 5-20.

After the design to be used has been selected, the next step is to reverse the design. The design must be carved in reverse so it will print correctly.

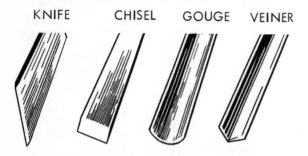

KNIFE   CHISEL   GOUGE   VEINER

Fig. 5-18. Linoleum block carving tools.

Fig. 5-19. Bookplate design which is suitable for linoleum block printing.

Fig. 5-20. Linoleum block design suggestions.

The reversing may be done by placing a piece of carbon paper on the back of the design with the carbon side up, and tracing over it with a pencil or ball point pen.

The design in reverse is then transferred to the linoleum block, using carbon paper, Fig. 5-21. If it is difficult to see the lines on the block, white dressmakers carbon paper may be used.

Next comes carving of the linoleum. So that you can see for yourself how the tools

CARBON

LINO-
LEUM

WOOD
BLOCK

Fig. 5-21. *Tracing design onto linoleum block.*

work in linoleum, it is advisable to experiment for a few minutes by carving on scrap stock. When you start carving your bookmark or other design, the first step is to outline the pattern, using a carving

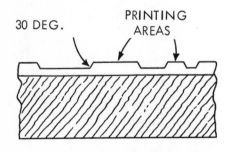

30 DEG.

PRINTING
AREAS

Fig. 5-22. *In outlining design, cuts should be made at an angle of about 30 degrees.*

knife. Work at an angle of about 30 deg. to provide a supporting shoulder, Fig. 5-22.

Take the gouge and pare away the linoleum close to the lines. The veiner may be used to tool narrow lines into the print-

BOOKPLATE OF
JOE BROWN

Fig. 5-23. *Print made from linoleum plate.*

ing area. The chisel will come in handy when clearing larger areas. Take shallow cuts, and be careful not to dig into the printing area. Linoleum should be removed from the non-printing surface to a depth of at least 1/16 in. The tools must be kept sharp, as dull chisels tend to push the linoleum instead of cutting it. The block is proofed, using a regular proof press, and any required corrections are made. After that, the block can be locked up and printed on a press like a regular type form. See Fig. 5-23.

Fig. 5-24. *Type locked up in special chase, for use in making a rubber stamp.*

MAKING RUBBER STAMPS

A second method of making printing plates with a minimum amount of equipment is the making of a rubber stamp, or a rubber printing plate.

The procedure for making a matrix for a rubber stamp is almost identical to making a matrix for a stereotype or an electrotype, but different materials are used.

Step #1 in making a rubber stamp is to set in type the words that will become the stamp. This type is then locked up in the special chase that comes with the press, as in Fig. 5-24. Note the type has type-high bearers locked up around the type. These can be 12 pt. brass rule, the same length as the type line or lines.

All rubber stamp presses require heat. The press should be heated to the temperature specified by the manufacturer.

Cut a piece of matrix material to the proper size to cover the type lines and the bearers. This matrix material is a special thermosetting plastic that softens during the first minute or so of the molding cycle, then with further heat and pressure hard-

ens to make a permanent mold or matrix of the type form.

The special chase, with the matrix material over the type form, is placed in the rubber stamp press. If shims are necessary to bring the form to the proper height, be sure they are included before clamping the press into the molding position. With everything in place, the clamps are lowered into the matrix-forming position, as shown in Fig. 5-25. The press is left in this position for the correct length of time. Consult manufacturer's manual.

Fig. 5-25. *Rubber stamp press in matrix-forming position.*

When the correct time has elapsed, the thermosetting plastic matrix material has formed and further heat will not change the molded image. The chase and the matrix are removed from the press. The molded image is checked, Fig. 5-26.

The next step requires a piece of rubber stamp gum. The rubber is cut to the correct size which is a little larger than the type lines. Be sure to put a small quantity of matrix release powder on the rubber

.Fig. 5-26. *Checking completed plastic matrix.*

gum before the stamp forming operation. This powder will assure you of being able to release the stamp from the matrix after the forming and vulcanizing process.

The matrix and the rubber are placed on a compensating block, (metal block that takes up the same space as the type when it was in the press). This is placed in the press and clamped, the same as the matrix-forming operation. It is left in the

press for the length of time indicated by the manufacturer. After the stamp has been formed and vulcanized, it is removed from the press, and carefully pulled loose from the matrix. Fig. 5-27.

Fig. 5-27. *Above. Removing rubber stamp from matrix. Below, Matrix and completed stamp (completed stamp is the one in reverse).*

The excess rubber around the type is trimmed away with scissors. The final step is to mount the rubber on a piece of stamp cushion molding which serves as a handle for the stamp. Saw molding to the correct size, Fig. 5-28.

SAMMY SAFETY
Says:

"In working around a hot rubber stamp press be careful not to get burned. Always wear heavy gloves when handling hot objects."

Fig. 5-28. *Sawing cushion molding (handle stock) to proper length.*

Fig. 5-29. Using completed rubber stamp.

The rubber stamp and the cushion mount are each coated with rubber cement and allowed to dry. The pieces are then stuck together. Fig. 5-29 shows the finished rubber stamp in use.

The ends of the mount stock are sanded and stained to match the color of the moulding mount.

RUBBER PRINTING PLATE

If the rubber stamp is to be used for printing on a press, it must be mounted on a block and brought up to type high. It may then be locked up in the chase and printed just like a type form.

ACTIVITIES

LINOLEUM BLOCK CUTTING

Information

In this activity you will have the opportunity to choose the type of project you want to work on. The new element is that the project must have a linoleum block illustration. If this is your first time working with linoleum it would be best to keep your linoleum design simple.

Practical Work

Choose a job requiring an illustration which may be reproduced by linoleum block printing.

Make a layout and plan sheet

Cut paper to print at least 25 copies

Remember the linoleum block design must be reversed

RUBBER STAMP MAKING

Information

This assignment will require setting in type the copy to be used for your stamp. The completed mold may be used as a rubber stamp, or a rubber printing plate. Be sure to check with your instructor as to type suitable for use in the stamp making process.

Practical work

Make a layout and plan sheet for a rubber stamp.

QUIZ - UNIT 5

1. Two typesetting machines commonly used in commercial print shops are _____ and the _____.
2. Describe briefly, how a Monotype machine works.
3. What is the principal difference between the type slugs cast by a Ludlow machine, and a Linotype?
4. A cold-type machine is one that sets type without the use of _____.
5. A line engraving is a photoengraving used to print _____.
6. A halftone is used to print _____.
7. Two types of duplicate printing plates are _____ and _____.
8. What are the principal requirements for making linoleum-block printing plates?
9. Describe briefly the procedure to follow in making a rubber stamp.

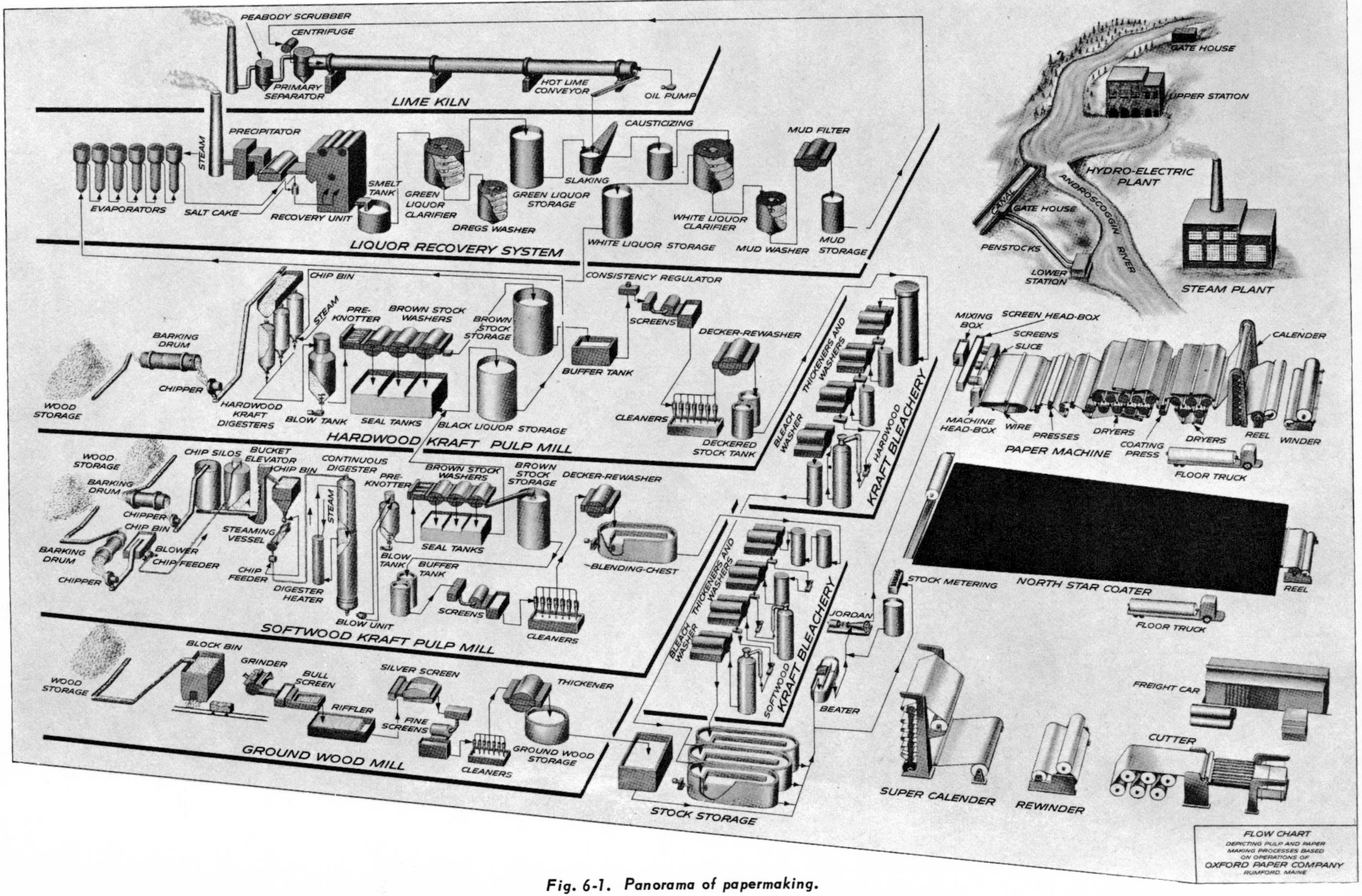

FLOW CHART
DEPICTING PULP AND PAPER
MAKING PROCESSES BASED
ON OPERATIONS OF
OXFORD PAPER COMPANY
RUMFORD, MAINE

GATE HOUSE
UPPER STATION
HYDRO-ELECTRIC PLANT
STEAM PLANT
ANDROSCOGGIN RIVER
LOWER STATION
GATE HOUSE
PENSTOCKS

CALENDER
WINDER
REEL
DRYERS
FLOOR TRUCK
REEL
DRYERS
COATING PRESS
FLOOR TRUCK
PAPER MACHINE
MIXING BOX
SCREEN HEAD-BOX
SCREENS
SLICE
MACHINE HEAD-BOX
WIRE
PRESSES
STOCK METERING
NORTH STAR COATER
SUPER CALENDER
REWINDER
FREIGHT CAR
CUTTER

MUD FILTER
MUD WASHER STORAGE
WHITE LIQUOR CLARIFIER
CAUSTICIZING
OIL PUMP
HOT LIME CONVEYOR
SLAKING
WHITE LIQUOR STORAGE
GREEN LIQUOR STORAGE
DREGS WASHER
GREEN LIQUOR CLARIFIER
SMELT TANK
RECOVERY UNIT
SALT CAKE
LIME KILN
LIQUOR RECOVERY SYSTEM
PEABODY SCRUBBER
CENTRIFUGE
PRIMARY SEPARATOR
PRECIPITATOR
STEAM
EVAPORATORS

HARDWOOD KRAFT BLEACHERY
BLEACH WASHER
THICKENERS AND WASHERS
DECKER-REWASHER
DECKERED STOCK TANK
CLEANERS
SCREENS
CONSISTENCY REGULATOR
BUFFER TANK
BROWN STOCK STORAGE
BLACK LIQUOR STORAGE
HARDWOOD KRAFT PULP MILL
PRE-KNOTTER
BROWN STOCK WASHERS
SEAL TANKS
HARDWOOD KRAFT DIGESTERS
BLOW TANK
STEAM
CHIP BIN
CHIPPER
BARKING DRUM
WOOD STORAGE

SOFTWOOD KRAFT BLEACHERY
BLEACH WASHER
THICKENERS AND WASHERS
JORDAN
BEATER
STOCK STORAGE
BLENDING-CHEST
DECKER-REWASHER
BROWN STOCK STORAGE
CLEANERS
SCREENS
SEAL TANKS
BUFFER TANK
BLOW TANK
BLOW UNIT
SOFTWOOD KRAFT PULP MILL
BROWN STOCK WASHERS
CONTINUOUS DIGESTER
PRE-KNOTTER
STEAM
CHIP BIN
DIGESTER HEATER
CHIP FEEDER
STEAMING VESSEL
CHIP BIN
CHIP FEEDER
BLOWER
CHIPPER
BARKING DRUM
CHIPPER
CHIP BIN
CHIP SILOS
BUCKET ELEVATOR
WOOD STORAGE

THICKENER
GROUND WOOD STORAGE
FINE SCREENS
CLEANERS
SILVER SCREEN
RIFFLER
BULL SCREEN
GRINDER
BLOCK BIN
GROUND WOOD MILL
WOOD STORAGE

Fig. 6-1. Panorama of papermaking.

PRINTING PAPER AND INK

1. How printing paper is made commercially.
2. Papermaking in the classroom.
3. Kinds of printing paper.
4. Basic sizes and weights of paper.
5. Printing inks.

MATERIALS USED IN MAKING PAPER

The principal raw materials from which printing papers are made, are wood pulp obtained from such trees as fir, spruce hemlock, poplar, pine and tamrack; and cotton fiber from the cotton plant. High-grade writing paper and paper used for documents usually contains a high rag content.

Commercial papermaking as it is done today is a complex process, as shown by the Panorama of Papermaking, Fig. 6-1, on the preceding page.

Fig. 6-2. *Papermaking in the classroom--using an egg beater to mix pulp solution.*

PAPERMAKING IN THE CLASSROOM

While making paper in a modern mill is an involved procedure, you can get a good idea of how wood pulp is formed into sheets by using simple equipment.

As your basic material you may use wood pulp obtained from a paper mill (dried pulp is kept on hand for experimental

Fig. 6-3. *Mold and deckle used in forming wet fibers into sheet.*

purposes by many graphic arts departments).

The first step in your papermaking experiment, is to put some of the wood pulp in a pan or tub of at least two-gallon capacity. Fill the pan about half full of water.

The pulp is mixed until the solution is free from lumps, using an ordinary egg beater, Fig. 6-2.

The wet fibers are formed into a sheet using a mold and deckle, as shown in Fig. 6-3. The deckle, shown at the right of the photo, consists of a light frame covered with fine-mesh screen; and the deckle shown at the left, is a larger frame into which the mold is fitted. In use the combined mold and deckle is slid into the pulp

Fig. 6-4. *Placing newly formed sheet of paper on blotter.*

solution at a slight angle until it is completely submerged. It is then brought to a flat position, slowly, shaking it from side to side to form the wood fiber into an even layer. The mold is placed on a table, and the deckle is lifted from the mold. The

Fig. 6-6. *Top, A warm iron is used to dry the newly formed sheet of paper. Fig. 6-7. Center, Sizing paper with glue and water solution. Fig. 6-8. Bottom, Finished sheet of hand-made paper.*

the sheet of paper to the desired thickness, to help force out excess moisture.

The next step is to remove the blotters from the press, and place the new paper between two sheets of smooth, uncoated paper and iron it dry with a warm (not hot) iron, Fig. 6-6. The dried sheet is then submerged just a second, into a 5 per cent glue and water mixture, as in Fig. 6-7. This sizes the sheet so you can write on it with ink. The sheet is again ironed dry with a warm iron. The completed hand made sheet is shown in Fig. 6-8.

KINDS OF PRINTING PAPER

Printing paper comes in an astonishing variety of types, weights, textures, colors and prices. It is important to use the right paper for each job and to know in

Fig. 6-5. *Using press to squeeze paper.*

newly-formed sheet of paper is placed on a blotter. This is called couching. Fig. 6-4. Additional blotters are placed on both sides of the wet paper and it is put into a press, Fig. 6-5. The press is tightened to squeeze advance what paper will be used so the job can be planned accordingly.

Some of the kinds of printing papers available for use today are:

NEWSPRINT

Newsprint paper is, as the name applies, used for printing newspapers and handbills. It is an inexpensive paper made from groundwood pulp.

BOOKPAPERS

Bookpapers come in many different weights and finishes, ranging from soft, porous sheets to the finest grades of smooth, coated papers. Book papers are used for printing books, magazines, catalogs, programs and pamphlets. Among the different kinds are the following:

MACHINE FINISHED BOOK, is an inexpensive bookpaper, but a better grade paper than newsprint.

SUPERCALENDERED BOOK, is a sized paper, made so it will not absorb ink. A better grade than machine finished paper.

SIZED AND SUPERCALENDERED, is like supercalendered paper but has a harder finish. It is better for printing halftones or pictures.

COATED ENAMEL, is used for reproducing fine halftone work.

OFFSET PAPER, is specially made for the offset process; a water resistant paper.

ANTIQUE PAPER, is a bulky, soft, porous paper. It is used chiefly for books where no pictures are necessary. Also used for programs.

ENGLISH FINISHED PAPER resembles the antique paper, but is smoother and less bulky.

WRITING PAPERS

Writing papers are made to take ink, pencil and printing inks. Some writing papers contain rag fibers (these are called rag content papers). Writing papers are known as Bonds, Ledgers, and Mimeograph Bonds.

CARDBOARDS

These papers are thick stiff papers used for ticket stock, file cards and poster paper.

INDEX AND PRINTING BRISTOLS are used for printing jobs requiring stiffness such as, die cut items, ticket and file cards.

RAILROAD BOARD is a heavy stock used for tickets, pamphlets, and book covers.

CHIPBOARD is an inexpensive gray-colored board used on the back of tablets.

COVER PAPERS

Cover papers are thicker than book papers and not as thick as cardboards. They come in many finishes such as: ripple, laid, coated and plate. They are used for covers as well as menus, bulletins, and catalogs.

MISCELLANEOUS PAPERS

There are many other papers and these fall into the miscellaneous paper class. These include: gummed papers with glue coating on one side, thin papers used for second sheets and air mail letters, and blotter stock which is a thick absorbent sheet.

BASIC SIZES AND WEIGHTS

A ream or 500 sheets of paper is the weight standard for paper used by printers. Paper comes in many different stock sizes and in a number of different weights. Special sizes are made to order. Each type of paper stock has a different BASIC size. Let's see what we mean by that statement. When we speak of 70 lb. book stock, it means that 500 sheets of this paper, in size 25 x 38, weigh 70 lbs. 25 x 38 is the basic size. When we refer to a 28 lb. bond, it means that 500 sheets of this paper 17 x 22 weigh 28 lbs. For bond paper, 17 x 22, is the basic size.

The table, Fig. 6-9, will enable you to tell at a glance, the comparative weights of different types of stock. You will note that a 70 lb. book stock, a 38 lb. cover, and a 28 lb. bond, are all about the same weight and thickness.

PRINTING INKS

Ink is a very important part of a finished printing job. Terms used in dealing with printing inks, with which you should become familiar are:

PIGMENT: Substance in ink which gives it color. Ink pigments may be organic (animal or vegetable matter), or inorganic (mineral matter).

VEHICLE (VARNISH): Liquid into which colored pigment is mixed. Ink vehicles include: linseed oil, tung oil, rosin, pitch, asphalt, gum.

DRIER: Substance added to ink to help control the drying time. Driers are obtained principally from metallic salts such as cobalt, manganese and lead. Ink dries by absorption (seeps into pores of the paper stock), Evaporation (liquid portion turns to vapor and escapes), and by Oxidation (vehicle in ink absorbs oxygen from the air causing liquid to turn to a solid).

Printing ink is essentially a mixture of vehicle or varnish pigment, and drier. The desired properties of ink vary according to the type of printing and press being used.

BASIC SIZE — CLASSIFICATION	Comparative weight scale
25 x 38 — Book	20 30 40 50 60 70 80 90 100 110 120 130
20 x 26 — Cover	10 20 30 40 50 60 65 70
17 x 22 — Bond	7 10 12 16 20 24 28 32 36 40 44 48
24 x 36 — Tag	20 30 40 50 60 70 80 90 100 110
22½ x 35 — Bristol	20 30 40 50 60 70 80 90 100
22½ x 28½ — Bristol	20 30 40 50 60 70 80
25½ x 30½ — Index	20 30 40 50 60 70 80 90 100
25 x 38 — Book	130 140 150 160 170 180 190 200 210 220 230 240
20 x 26 — Cover	70 80 90 100 110 120 130
17 x 22 — Bond	52 56 60 64 68 72 76 80 84 88 92
24 x 36 — Tag	120 130 140 150 160 170 180 190 200 210
22½ x 35 — Bristol	110 120 125 130 140 150 160 170 175 180 190 200
22½ x 28½ — Bristol	90 100 110 120 130 140 150 160
25½ x 30½ — Index	110 120 130 140 150 160 170 180 190

Fig. 6-9. Comparative weights of various kinds of paper.
(James White Paper Co.)

In general, the basic requirements are:

1. Uniform consistency.

2. Viscosity (rate of flow) suited to the speed of the press and rate at at which it is to be applied.

3. Drying qualities as required to prevent smudging and to permit handling of the printed sheets within a reasonable time.

Printing inks may be divided into three main classes: Letterpress, Lithographic, and Gravure, corresponding to the three major types of printing presses. Inks are made to be used on specific kinds of presses and for specific kinds of paper. Ink types available include:

NEWS INK: For news stock, a soft bodied ink that dries by soaking into the stock.

JOB INK: A stiff ink to be used on job presses for the average run of work.

BOND: A very stiff ink for use on bond and ledger papers.

HALFTONE INK: A smooth, soft ink for use on coated papers and for printing halftones.

COVER INK: A very stiff, full-bodied ink used on cover paper where good coverage is necessary.

SPECIALTY INK: Special inks for special purposes. For such materials as cellophane and wax papers.

If it is necessary to mix inks to get a certain color, be sure to start with the lightest color, and add a small quantity of the darker color to it.

Always take ink from the top of the can, leaving the remaining ink flat. Put a piece of wax paper over the top of the ink to keep it from drying.

ACTIVITY

MAKING A SHEET OF PAPER

Information:

In this activity you will make a sheet of paper by following the directions in this unit. As you do each step, try to relate it to the industrial process. Be sure to paste up your completed paper and answer the questions in the Quiz, before turning it in to your instructor.

Practical Work

Obtain pulp from your instructor and place in a tub with water for beating. When pulp is the right consistency, follow directions in this unit for making a hand made sheet of paper.

QUIZ - UNIT 6

1. The principal raw materials from which paper is made are___ and ____.
2. Describe the use of a mold and deckle in making paper in the classroom.
3. Five kinds of paper used by print shops are _____.
4. A____or_____sheets is the weight standard for paper used by printers.
5. The basic size for book paper is ___, for bond paper _____.
6. The substance in ink that gives it color is the _____.
7. What do we mean when we say that a certain ink dries by absorption, by oxidation?
8. Printing inks may be divided into three main classes: Letterpress, ____, and _____.

LITHOGRAPHIC PRINTING

UNIT 7

1. Principle of lithographic printing.
2. Copy preparation.
3. Offset equipment used by industry.
4. Making a lithographic print in the classroom.

Lithography is an important printing process.

This type of printing is different from letterpress printing, yet the results produced are similar. In lithographic printing, the design is reproduced on a flat printing plate.

The design on the plate is neither raised nor sunken, Fig. 7-1. It is the same height

PRINTING SURFACE

Fig. 7-1. Lithographic printing. Paper is pressed against a flat surface. Only the printing areas ink up, because the non-printing areas of the plate are treated to repel the ink.

as the blank, non-printing areas around it. The non-printing areas of the plate do not print because they are chemically treated to repel the ink.

As we discussed briefly in Unit 1, lithography is based on the simple princi-

ple that oil or grease, and water will not mix.

An example will help to make this principle clear. Let's suppose you poured some red fountain pen ink in a pan of water. What would happen? The ink would mix with the water and the water would turn red. If you poured some thin red oil paint into a pan of water the color would not mix with the water--because oil and water will not mix. The color would float on the surface in a kind of greasy design. It would be easy to transfer this design to paper were you to place a sheet of paper on the water, it would absorb the color. This principle is used in binderies for "marbleizing" the edges of books.

The marbleizing is similar in principle to lithographic printing. However, because the water is fluid and the image is unstable, it is impossible to produce a number of prints that are the same. The image must be fixed or anchored to a solid material, such as a lithographic plate.

Early experiments in lithography led to the development of the rotary press, which consisted of two cylinders that rotated in the same direction. The plate was carried on one, and the paper on the other. This press raised production to about 1,000 impressions per hour. All lithographic printing was done like this until 1906, when Ira Rubel, a lithographer at Nutley, N. J. developed a press that would print much faster, using the OFFSET principle. How this principle works in a rotary press is shown in Fig. 7-2.

An offset printing unit consists of an ink fountain and rollers, a water fountain and rollers, and three large metal cylinders. The printing plate is attached to the top cylinder; a rubber blanket is attached to the center cylinder, and the bottom cylinder carries the paper through the press, forcing it against the rubber blanket to make a printed impression.

When the press is turned on, the cylinders revolve, and the plate is carried under the dampening rollers, the inking rollers, and finally against the rubber blanket. The dampening rollers thus keep the non-printing areas of the plate wet so they will not take ink when the plate passes under the ink rollers. As a result

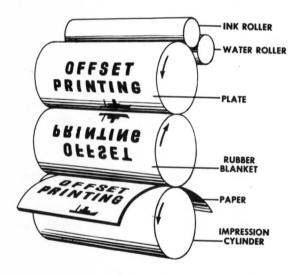

Fig. 7-2. Principle of offset printing.

only the image is inked. After the plate has passed under the ink rollers it contacts the blanket cylinder, transferring the inked image to the blanket. The blanket in turn, offsets or prints the wet image on the paper which is forced against it by the impression cylinder.

In offset printing the image faces right at the start. The impression is made on the blanket in reverse. The blanket then offsets an image on the paper which reads right.

MANY DIFFERENT NAMES

Lithographic processes are called by many different names - planography, photolithography, zincography, etc. If the lithographic printing is done on an offset press from a lithographic plate, it is called OFFSET PRINTING. If photography was used in making the plate, it becomes photo-offset printing. It is not photo-offset unless photography is involved in making the plate.

PLANNING JOB FOR OFFSET PRINTING

The first step in planning a job for offset printing is to plan the job.

For offset printing, type has to be set and illustrations must be obtained.

A layout must be provided which shows the arrangement of the various elements. The type may be set by hand or on a hot-metal machine as described for letterpress and reproduction proofs pulled; PHOTOTYPE or, by using what is called COLD-TYPE composition.

PHOTOTYPESETTING MACHINES

Phototypesetting machines are used for composition just as the regular hot metal machines are used, but the product obtained is reproduction of type on film. In operating a phototypesetting machine, as shown in Fig. 7-3, as the operator presses keys on the machine, photographic matrices fall into place in the line. Each matrix carries a small film negative of the letter it represents.

The phototypesetting machine, as shown in Fig. 7-3a has two units, a keyboard and photo unit. The operator punches tape at the keyboard unit. The tape is fed into the photo unit which produces film negatives.

COLD TYPESETTING MACHINES

There are available on the market a number of machines that produce material which closely resembles the type set by conventional type machines. One of these

Fig. 7-3. An Intertype phototypesetting machine which provides reproduction of type on film.

Fig. 7-3a. Mergenthaler Linofilm keyboard and photo unit.

machines is the Varityper, shown in Fig. 7-4. When a key on a Verityper is pressed, a small moon-shaped type plate on which

are all the letters of the alphabet, is rotated quickly to bring the proper letter into position. The type does not strike the paper as in a typewriter, but instead, the machine forces the paper against the type. The type plates are easily changed, making it possible to use the machine for setting a variety of different type faces. The Varityper furnishes proofs ready for

Fig. 7-4. A Vari-Typer which features quick change of type faces.

pasteup. Or, it may be used to type directly onto duplicating machine plates.

Another machine used to handle composition for offset printing is the Justowriter, shown in Fig. 7-5. As the copy is typed on one machine (recorder) a tape is

Fig. 7-5. Friden Justowriter. Left. Recorder. Right. Reproducer.

punched and coded for spacing. The tape is run through a second machine (reproducer) where the copy is automatically retyped and justified in one operation. A Justowrtier sets type in just one face like a typewriter.

You may be interested in learning that the captions for this book were set on a Varityper, and the body of text matter, on a Justowriter.

In getting material ready for plate making, the line illustrations and type matter

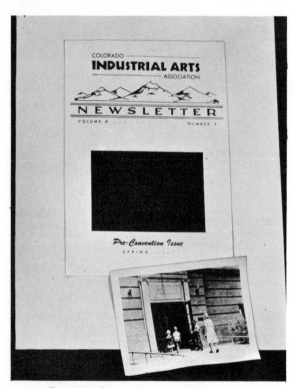

Fig. 7-6. Copy to be printed offset, which is ready for the camera.

are pasted in position, as in Fig. 7-6. This pasteup is then copied with a camera. The line copy is photographed separately from the photo, or halftone copy. In photographing the line copy, the area in which the halftone is to be placed is covered (solid black area of Fig. 7-6) to form a window for the halftone negative.

The halftone and line negatives are stripped together in their proper printing positions on a sheet of goldenrod or orange masking paper, Fig. 7-7. Windows

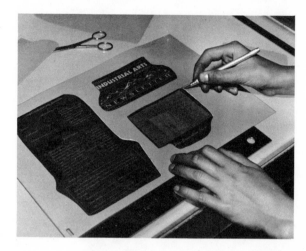

Fig. 7-7. Line and halftone copy being stripped together on sheet of golden masking paper.

are cut in the paper to expose the printing areas of the negatives.

The next step occurs in the plate room. The plate maker may use a pre-sensitized plate or take a thin zinc plate that has been grained (roughened by grinding with abrasives so it will hold moisture) and coat it with a light-sensitive solution. As soon as it dries he places it in a vacuum-printing frame, and positions the negative assembly over it. He then exposes it to a bright light, Fig. 7-8.

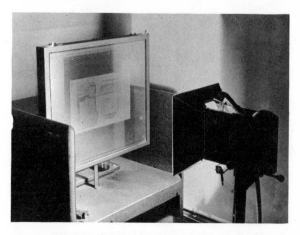

Fig. 7-8. Making plate for offset printing.

Fig. 7-9. *Direct image plates. Left, Looped-end plate used by Multilith. Right, Plate with straight edge used by Davidson Press.*

During the exposure, the light passes through the transparent areas of the negative and hardens the coating on the plate wherever it strikes. After the exposure is ended, the operator removes the plate from the printing frame, and develops it according to the instructions supplied by the manufacturer of the developer being used. The plate is soaked in water to dissolve the unhardened area of the coating. The light-hardened areas remain on the plate as the printing image. The plate is then ready for printing.

DIRECT-IMAGE PLATES

Also available for offset printing are paper and plastic Direct-Image plates, Fig. 7-9. In using these plates the copy is typed or drawn right on the plate, eliminating the photographic operation.

PRESSES FOR OFFSET PRINTING

In the pressroom, the offset plate is

Fig. 7-10. *Above, Offset press made by Davidson Corp. Below, Offset press made by Harris-Intertype Corp.*

clamped onto the cylinder of the press. The procedure in operating the press varies according to the type of equipment being used, but the lithographic principle which we learned--OIL WILL NOT MIX WITH WATER, is the basis of the printing done by all of them.

Several types of offset presses are shown in Figs. 7-10, and 7-11.

Fig. 7-12. First step in making lithographic print is to reverse the design. This is necessary because the print will be reversed in printing only once, as in letterpress printing. Place a piece of carbon paper back of the design with the carbon side up, and trace over the design. This traces the design in reverse on the back of the design sheet. Using carbon paper again, trace the reversed design onto direct-image plate.

Fig. 7-11. Above, Large sheet-fed Miehle offset press. Center, Large sheet-fed offset press made by Harris-Intertype Corp. Below, Web-fed offset press made by the Goss Co.

MAKING A LITHOGRAPHIC PRINT

You can get some first-hand knowledge of the lithographic principle by making a lithographic print. This job is intended particularly for graphic arts departments in schools that do not have access to offset printing equipment.

The step-by-step procedure in making such a print is shown by the photos and captions, Figs. 7-12, to 7-20 inclusive.

Fig. 7-13. Going over lines to be printed, using a litho-reproducing pencil.

Fig. 7-14. Spreading litho ink on glass slab, and inking brayer.

Fig. 7-15. Using sponge to moisten plate with fountain solution. The plate must be damp---not wet.

Fig. 7-16. While plate is still damp, it is inked ready for printing. Moistened sponge may be used to pick up ink specks from non-printing area. If brayer picks up too much water and will not transfer ink to plate, excess water may be removed by rolling brayer over sheet of newspaper.

Fig. 7-17. Making print with etching press. Press and paper are run through press under slight pressure.

Fig. 7-18. Making print on type proof press. Block is placed under litho plate to bring it up to regular type height.

Fig. 7-19. Pulling print and plate apart. The print is put under a weight to straighten it.

Fig. 7-20. Comparing finished print (left), with design on lithographic plate.

ACTIVITY

LITHOGRAPHIC PRINTING

Information

Choose or make a design that will be suitable for making a lithographic print.

Practical work

1. Choose design
2. Reverse design and transfer to plate
3. Cut paper for prints (at least 6)
4. Prepare ink and fountain solution
5. Dampen plate
6. Ink plate
7. Make print
8. Mount print

A finished print may be mounted for showing. To mount the print a paper or cardboard frame is put around the print to finish it off so that it will give a good appearance. Use a paper with a textured finish or regular mat board if available. Leave about 1 in. showing around the print on top and sides, and about 1-1/2 in. on the bottom. Cut a window out of the mat material and leave about 3 in. of mat material on top and sides and about 4 in. on the bottom. These dimensions can vary with the style of your print.

QUIZ - UNIT 7

1. In lithographic printing the design is reproduced from a printing plate on which the printing area is different height than the non-printing area. True or false?
2. Lithography is based on the principle that_____.
3. How does offset printing differ from regular lithographic printing?
4. In preparing copy for offset printing, do you start with the image facing right, or reversed?
5. Cold-type composition is produced by methods that make use of type metal and metal slugs. True or false?
6. In making a plate for offset printing, the plate maker takes a thin zinc plate that has been grained. What do we mean by grained?
7. How does a direct-image plate differ from a regular zinc offset plate?
8. In making a lithographic print in the classroom, is it necessary to reverse the design? Why?
9. Describe procedure for inking plate used in making lithographic print in the classroom.

INTAGLIO (GRAVURE) PRINTING

1. Intaglio printing principle.
2. How the intaglio industry produces its printing.
3. Making an intaglio print in the classroom.

We have discussed printing in industry using a raised printing surface, called Letterpress printing; also using a Flat surface part of which has been treated to take ink, called Lithography.

This Unit deals with a third method, printing from a depressed design, called Intaglio printing. See Fig. 8-1, also refer back to Fig. 1-6, page 6. The word

Fig. 8-1. In intaglio printing, the design to be reproduced on paper is engraved or etched below the surface of the printing plate.

intaglio is pronounced in-tal'yo. To describe this type of printing, the industry uses such terms as Copper and Steel Engraving, Gravure, Rotogravure, and Photogravure.

COPPER AND STEEL ENGRAVING

In copper and steel engraving, letters are engraved or etched into a flat metal plate, leaving depressions or wells. Ink is

Fig. 8-2. Copper plating a cylinder of a rotogravure press. (Denver Post).

squeezed into these depressions, the excess ink is wiped from the plate, then under pressure, the ink is forced onto the paper. The copper and steel engraving industry produces such items as fine letterheads, social stationery, professional calling cards and social announcements.

ROTOGRAVURE PRINTING

Rotogravure is used on such jobs as special sections for newspapers, magazines, and catalogs. It is used also for printing wallpaper, textiles, cellophane, aluminum foil and wax paper. Sheet-fed gravure printing is used to print our money.

Rotogravure has its limitations in that the printing plates are very expensive to prepare. This process is best suited for work that requires long runs (many thousands of copies).

Several of the steps required to get a rotogravure press cylinder ready for printing are illustrated. Fig. 8-2, shows

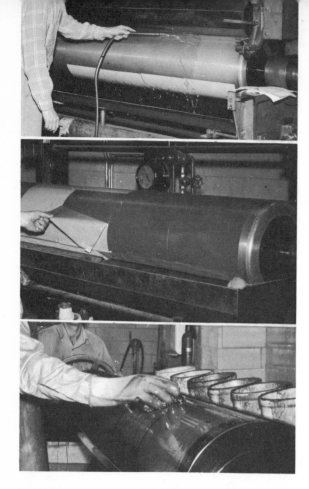

Fig. 8-3. Top, Placing carbon tissue on copper plated cylinder of rotogravure press. Fig. 8-4. Center, Removing backing paper from surface of carbon tissue. Fig. 8-5. Bottom, Etching designs into cylinder.

copper plating of a press cylinder. After plating, the cylinder is polished smooth to provide a good printing surface. Negatives and positives are prepared in a camera room.

Instead of sensitizing the copper cylinder, a special material known as carbon tissue is sensitized, and the image and screen pattern are exposed to this carbon tissue material. The screen pattern is exposed to the tissue first, then a continuous tone positive is exposed to the same material. This makes the dot pattern in gravure work different than the dot pattern used in letterpress and lithography. In gravure printing everything is screened, even the type matter.

The carbon tissue is then put on the copper plated cylinder in a machine called the laydown machine, Fig. 8-3. This de-

vice allows the carbon tissue to be put in register so the pages will print correctly. If color is used, it will print in the correct position.

After the carbon tissue has been put in place, the backing paper is removed leaving just the gelatin surface with the image on the cylinder. This is called developing, see Fig. 8-4. This becomes an acid-resist material. The cylinder is put into an etching bath, which etches the wells into the copper. Fig. 8-5 shows this operation. The light areas of the picture allow only a shallow etch; the dark areas allow a deeper etch. Hand work called staging is frequently necessary in order to complete the plate.

A film recently introduced to the trade called Rotofilm, is being used in some shops in place of carbon tissue. The processes are the same, but the Rotofilm appears as a visible image before being transferred to the cylinder. This helps in quality control.

The cylinders are put in their proper places on a rotary gravure press such as shown in Fig. 8-6. This press uses rolls of paper and can print many thousands of copies per hour. The ink is in a fountain and is sprayed on the cylinder. A doctor blade (scraper) removes the excess ink so only the wells or recessed areas contain ink. This is then transferred to the paper.

The paper passes through driers between and after impressions. It is cut into sheets and folded by the press.

COLLOTYPE

In the collotype process, no halftone screen is used. Tone variation in the print has no screen pattern. Variation of tone is obtained by controlling the depth of etching in the printing plates. Collotype printing is used in making reproductions of photographs, and expensive paintings.

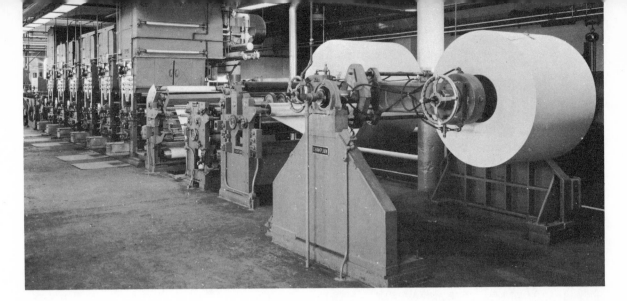

Fig. 8-6. A rotogravure press.
(Champlain Co.)

MAKING AN INTAGLIO PRINT (DRY POINT ETCHING) IN THE CLASSROOM

Intaglio printing requires large and expensive equipment that is usually not available for classroom use. For this reason it seldom is possible in a graphic arts department to work the actual equipment.

We can find out about the basic steps in such printing, however, by making a DRY POINT ETCHING. A dry point etching is an intaglio print made by hand, using a sharp-pointed instrument to tool or scratch a design into a plate. Plate material may be transparent celluloid or plastic (sheet acetate). Cleared X-ray film is satisfactory.

Fig. 8-8. Tools for making dry point etchings.

The first step in making a dry point etching is to obtain or draw up a suitable design---one that lends itself to line reproduction. See Fig. 8-7. For an etching tool you may use a sharp-pointed steel needle, such as a phonograph needle. The needle should be fitted into a wooden handle, or used in a pin vise. An old dental tool sharpened to a point, also makes an excellent etching tool, Fig. 8-8.

Fig. 8-7. Design to be reproduced in dry point etching.

Place the film material over the design and tape it in place. Since the plate is transparent, the design to be scratched into the plate is clearly visible. In scratching in the lines it is better to use a series of short lines rather than long lines. For dark areas, crosshatching of the lines will make the area print dark.

Fig. 8-9. Sliding piece of black paper between design and plate to check engraving.

To check the engraving as you proceed, slide a piece of black or dark-colored paper between the plate and the design, as in Fig. 8-9. Continue scratching in the

Fig. 8-10. Moistening paper to be used in making dry point etching.

lines until the design is engraved in the plate to your satisfaction. The plate is then ready to use in making a print.

Preparing the paper for making a dry point print is a very important step. Select a piece of antique book paper, and cut it to the correct size for your prints. The print size sheets are then soaked in water, and placed between pieces of blotter stock. A

Fig. 8-11. Mixing ink for dry point etching.

weight should be put on top of the blotters so they will stay flat. The paper should remain in the blotter sheets for about one hour before being used. To make a good print, the sheet should be damp clear through the sheet, but not wet. Moistening the paper for conditioning is shown in Fig. 8-10.

While the paper is conditioning, the ink for printing should be prepared. You can use an etchers ink, or some soft-bodied printing ink. Add a small quantity of plate oil or ink reducer to decrease the tack. This can be worked in with an ink knife, Fig. 8-11.

When the paper is ready, the plate can be inked. A piece of lint-free cloth, makes a good dabber to work the ink into the etched lines. Never slide or rub the dabber over the plate. Make sure all the lines contain ink.

After the plate is completely inked, it

is necessary to remove the surplus ink from the areas between the lines, the non-printing areas. In rotogravure printing on a press, this is done by the doctor blade, but in dry point, it is accomplished by wiping with paper toweling or with a clean, lint-free cloth. Wipe in straight strokes and not in circles or you will remove the ink from the lines, Fig. 8-12.

Fig. 8-13. Using etching press to make print.

Fig. 8-12. Removing ink from non-printing areas.

When most of the ink is removed, put a drop of plate oil on the palm of your hand and finish wiping the plate with the soft part of the palm.

Using an etching press to make a print is shown in Fig. 8-13. The adjusting screw on the press is tightened to give considerable pressure. A piece of felt which

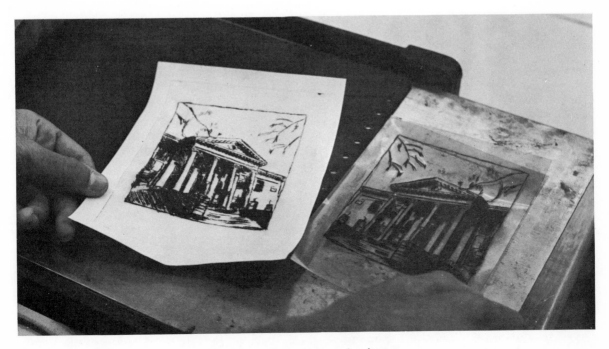

Fig. 8-14. Examining completed print.

Fig. 8-15. Design suggestions.

serves as a blanket is placed on the bed of the press, then the plate and the paper. Next comes the job you have been waiting for, the actual making of the print. Examine your print (made by the intaglio process) carefully, Fig. 8-14, then compare it with the original art.

Each time you make a print, all the steps, except the scratching of the plate must be repeated.

ACTIVITY

DRY-POINT ETCHING

Information

Choose or make a design that will be suitable for making a dry-point etching. Remember that the illustration should be one that lends itself to line reproduction.

Practical Work

1. Choose design
2. Engrave plate
3. Prepare and condition paper (make 6 prints)
4. Prepare ink
5. Ink plate
6. Wipe plate
7. Make extra prints
8. Mount one print

QUIZ - UNIT 8

1. Explain the principle of intaglio printing.
2. Copper and steel engravings are used in producing such items as_____(name three).
3. Why is rotogravure printing generally limited to work requiring long runs?
4. In intaglio printing, how is excess ink removed from the printing cylinder?
5. Is a halftone screen used in photogravure printing?
6. A dry point etching is_____.
7. Describe the step-by-step procedure for making a dry point etching plate.
8. In making a print, why is it necessary to remove the ink from the areas between the lines in the plate?
9. What steps must be repeated when making extra prints.

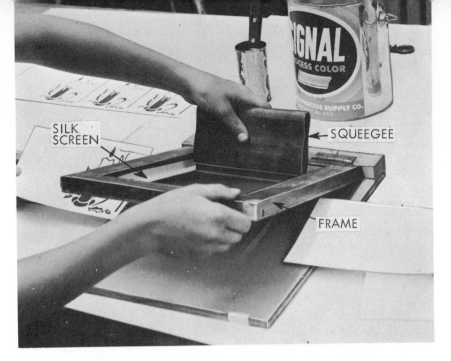

Fig. 9-1. *Three basic requirements for silk screen printing---Frame, Silk Screen, and a Squeegee to force printing medium through screen.*

SILK SCREEN PRINTING

UNIT 9

1. Principle of silk screen printing.
2. Some industrial uses of silk screen process.
3. Making a silk screen print in the classroom.

Silk screen printing is a very versatile, fast-growing member of the graphic arts industry. Using this process, it is possible to successfully print various thicknesses of board, glass, wood, plastic, leather, textile, as well as a host of other surface materials, regardless of size or shape of the material. The printing medium may be ink, paint, varnish, or lacquer.

Whether the printing is done with a simple printing unit, Fig. 9-1, or an automatic press, Fig. 9-2, the three basic requirements are the same:

1. Frame of wood, metal or plastic

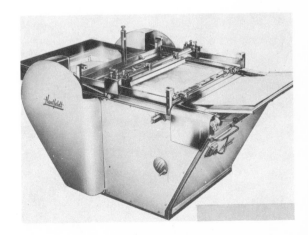

Fig. 9-2. *Automatic press for screen stencil printing. (Advance Process Supply Co.,Inc.)*

Fig. 9-3. Noel design being cut into transparent lacquer film.

to hold the screen.

2. Fine mesh, accurately woven silk or metal fabric screen.

3. Rubber or plastic squeegee for forcing printing medium through screen stencil.

Using the photographic stencil-making

Fig. 9-4. Laying out job for printing.

techniques and the press equipment available today, it is possible to print fine-line details, even four-color halftones.

Silk screen printing is also considered a fine art, and many fine prints are on display in art museums.

MAKING A SILK SCREEN PRINT IN THE CLASSROOM

To further pursue our policy of "learning by doing," we will describe the step-by-step procedure for making a silk screen print in the classroom, using simple equipment, such as shown in Fig. 9-1.

Making a silk screen print using this equipment requires about the same steps as other printing processes, but the details are, of course, different.

First we will need a suitable design--a heavy line or silhouette type of illustration, such as the Noel design, shown in Fig. 9-3. This process does not require that the design by reversed.

Next we must cover the non-printing areas of the silk with a lacquer film stencil. There are many stencil materials that may be used, but for this basic experience we suggest a lacquer film such as Pro-Film, or Nu-Film. These films have a lacquer coating on a wax paper base.

Cut a piece of the lacquer film to the proper size (film should be at least 2 in. larger each way than design) and tape it in place over the design which has also been secured with tape, see Fig. 9-3. The smooth or film side of the lacquer film should face the worker.

In cutting the design into the film, the knife used should be held as you would hold a pencil. This is also shown in Fig. 9-3. Cut along the lines and around the various areas of your design. Use light pressure on the knife so you will not cut through the wax paper backing.

Fig. 9-5. Left, Pieces of chipboard fastened to baseboard, serve as guides for stock. Fig. 9-6. Right, Positioning lacquer film.

When you have finished cutting around the various parts of the design, remove the lacquer film from the areas to be printed. These open areas allow the ink to pass through the silk screen to form the design. Do not remove the wax paper, just peel off the lacquer film.

The next step is to take the silk screen frame and design, and set the guides for printing. Place the original design which in most cases will be the same size as the paper to be used in printing, on the base board. The job must be laid out so the design will print on the stock in the proper location, Fig. 9-4. Now, mark off one end and one side for feeding guides. You can make guides from pieces of chipboard (heavy cardboard). These can be cemented to the base board with rubber cement. They should also be taped, using masking tape, Fig. 9-5. Fenders should be made from chipboard that may be used to strip the printed sheets from the silk screen.

The next operation is to adhere (fasten) the stencil to the silk. Place your original copy and layout against the guides in the printing position. Now put the stencil over the design. Use small pieces of cellophane tape to hold the lacquer film stencil in the exact position for printing, Fig. 9-6.

Remove your design and place several sheets of newspaper cut larger than your design, but smaller than the silk screen frame in position as shown in Fig. 9-7. Close the screen. Take two clean cloths, one for adhering, and one for rubbing down.

Adhering liquid is a special preparation that will cause the lacquer film to dissolve slightly and impregnate itself into the silk. Pour a very small amount on one cloth, and rub into a small area. This area should

Fig. 9-7. Newspaper sheets are used for padding when adhering lacquer film to silk.

be rubbed down immediately with the other cloth, Fig. 9-8. Repeat this until the design is completely adherred to the silk.

Pull the hinge pins on the silk screen frame and remove it from the base board. Turn the frame over. Fill in the areas not covered by the stencil with block-out solution, Fig. 9-9. Be sure not to remove the wax paper from the design until the blocking out is completed. Allow this block-out material to dry, then carefully remove the wax paper from your film, Fig.

Fig. 9-8. *Top, Adhering lacquer film to silk.* Fig. 9-9. *Center, Blocking out non-printing areas.* Fig. 9-10. *Bottom, Removing wax paper covering from lacquer film.*

9-10. Tape the outside edges of the silk screen from both the front and the back with masking tape as in Fig. 9-11.

Fig. 9-11. *Taping edges of stencil.*

The next operation will be to prepare the silk screen paint or ink for use. Manufacturers of this type of ink put it up in cans of various sizes and in almost all colors. Some of these inks require mixing with other ingredients to prepare them for the printing process. In mixing ink it is best to follow the manufacturer's recommendations.

MAKING PRINTS

Place your stock to be printed on one side of the silk screen frame. Provide some drying racks, or a suitable place to place the prints while drying. Pour into the frame the correct amount of ink (your instructor will advise you on this), Fig.

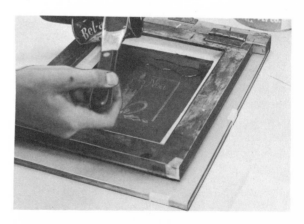

Fig. 9-12. *Inking screen printing press.*

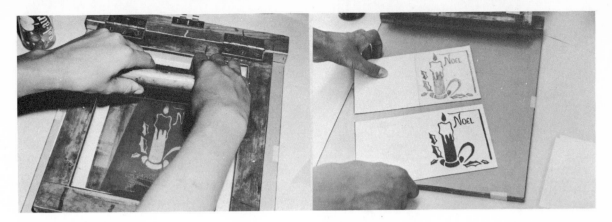

Fig. 9-13. Left, *Using squeegee to make a print.* Fig. 9-14, Right, *Comparing print (below) with original art.*

9-12. Insert a sheet of paper stock, and with the squeegee tilted forward so the sharp corner is actually scraping the ink, pull the squeegee toward you to make a print, as shown in Fig. 9-13. Compare the completed print with the original art to see if all the details are included. See Fig. 9-14.

Running off silk screen prints is a job where you can have two people help you; one to place the stock into the guides, and one to remove the printed sheets and place them to dry. Working as a team you can complete a number of prints in a short time.

To clean ink from the silk screen frame, but not remove the design, use rags moistened with a solvent that will not dissolve the lacquer film such as kerosene, mineral spirits or white gasoline.

With the printing completed, and the ink removed, you are now ready to remove the design from your screen and get it ready for another job.

The procedure is as follows: First place several sheets of newspaper under the silk screen frame. Pour a small amount of lacquer thinner on the top side of the frame. Place a piece of newspaper over this to keep the lacquer thinner from evaporating too fast. Allow to stand for about three to five minutes. Remove the newsprint. This will pick up a good portion of the block-out and the lacquer film design. Using additional sheets of newsprint stock, repeat the operation. Using rags moistened with lacquer thinner, rub on both sides of the screen as it is held in a vertical position, Fig. 9-15, remove the balance of the lacquer film from the screen.

SAMMY SAFETY
Says:

"In using solvent for removing ink and lacquer film from a silk screen be sure the room is well ventilated and that the necessary precautions are taken to prevent fire. Soiled rags must be stored in a safety can provided for the purpose. This is very important."

Fig. 9-15. *Using lacquer thinner to remove lacquer film from silk.*

Fig. 9-16. *Samples of silk screen prints that were done in a typical school shop setup.*

Your instructor will want to inspect your screen before you put it away.

MAKING STENCILS PHOTOGRAPHICALLY

The use of stencils made photographically extends the range of the screen process to the reproduction of fine line drawings and halftones.

The art work is photographed and a film positive is made. The positive is placed in contact with a special stencil material the top surface of which is a light-sensitive gelatin bonded to a backing. After exposure, the stencil is developed. The image portion of the stencil remains water soluble and is washed out. The stencil is then attached to the silk. When dry its protective support sheet is removed, and the stencil is ready for printing.

ACTIVITY

SILK SCREEN PRINTING

Information:

Choose a project suitable for silk screen printing. Some suggested projects include a monogram for stationery or paper napkins, posters, greeting cards, cover for a play or dance program, a cover for a graphic arts notebook, club membership cards.

If you would like to do this assignment in two colors, a separate stencil must be cut for each color and then registered so the colors will print in the proper place.

Practical Work:

1. Choose your design

2. Make a layout and procedure plan

3. Cut stencil and adhere to silk

4. Cut stock for printing

5. Print desired number of copies

6. Clean up silk screen

QUIZ - UNIT 9

1. Three basic requirements for silk screen printing are _____.
2. Is it necessary to reverse the design to be printed by the silk screen method? Why?
3. In preparing a silk screen stencil, for what purpose is a lacquer film used?
4. In adhering the completed lacquer stencil to the silk, rubber cement is used as an adhesive. True or false?
5. Tell how squeegee is used in making print.
6. In cleaning ink from a silk screen a solvent such as _____or_____ may be used.
7. What solvent is used when removing the lacquer film from the stencil?

BINDERY OPERATIONS

1. Operations performed in the bindery--paper cutting, folding, padding, binding.
2. Book binding in the classroom.
3. Commercial book binding.

The bindery is the end of the line for a job in a print shop. It is in the bindery department, or bindery section of the press room, where the stock is cut, punched, padded, perforated, or a cover put on. The finished job is then wrapped ready for delivery. Of course, not all of these operations are required for every job that goes through the print shop. Some jobs require but one simple operation, like wrapping for delivery.

PAPER CUTTING

Paper cutting is perhaps the most common of the bindery operations. Hand-lever cutters such as are found in small shops, and school shops are shown in Figs. 10-1

and 10-3. A large, power-operated cutter such as used by commercial shops is shown in Fig. 10-2.

OPERATING HAND LEVER CUTTER: In operating a cutter as shown in Fig. 10-3, the paper stock to be cut is loaded on the cutter table, against a metal bar at the back of the cutter called a Back Gauge. The back gauge can be regulated for width of cut by turning the hand wheel located under the cutting table. On some cutters a metal tape that travels with the back gauge can be read to determine depth of cut. On other

Fig. 10-1. Hand lever-operated paper cutter. (Chandler & Price Co.)

SAMMY SAFETY
Says:

"The blade of a paper cutter is sharp. The cutter must be operated with great care. Always obtain permission from your instructor before using the cutter. Make sure that no one but you is inside the operator's safety zone. Be certain the handle (lever) controlling the blade is in its proper position and safety lock is engaged before setting back gauge. Use care when jogging paper to avoid being cut by the sharp edges. Keep hands clear of blade at all times. Limit amount of stock to be cut at any one time. If one hand is not required to operate a safety device as in Fig. 10-4, keep both hands on the lever while making the cut, and returning lever to proper position. Check to see that safety lock engages after using cutter. Pay attention to what you are doing.....while operating a paper cutter is not the time or place to visit."

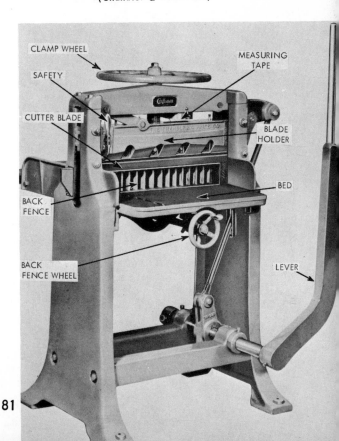

cutters a ruler or yardstick is used for measuring.

When the depth of cut is set and the hand wheel locked with a thumb screw, a clamping device (clamp) is brought down to hold the paper in place for the cut. The hand wheel on top of the cutter operates the clamp. To keep the paper from being marred by the clamp, and to make sure of getting a clean cut on the bottom sheets, pieces of cardboard are placed on both sides of the paper pile, or lift, as it is called.

Fig. 10-2. Large, power-operated paper cutter. (Lawson Co.)

Fig. 10-4. Operating paper cutter. Left hand is being used to operate safety device.

PAPER FOLDING

To meet today's needs, paper is folded in

Fig. 10-3. Jogging paper before placing it in cutter.

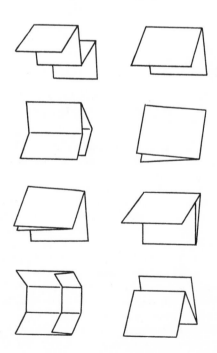

Fig. 10-5. Basic paper folds.

many different ways, The common basic folds are shown in Fig. 10-5.

In the school shop most folding is done by hand using a bone folder, Fig. 10-6. For commercial use folding machines come in

Fig. 10-6. Folding paper by hand, using bone folder.

many different sizes, and designs. A large commercial-type folder is shown in Fig. 10-7.

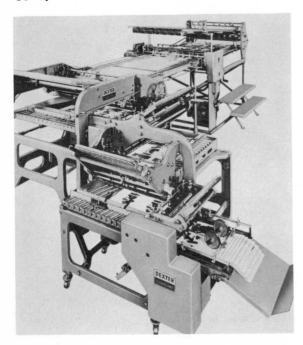

Fig. 10-7. Commercial-type paper folding machine. (Dexter Folder Co.)

BINDING

Types of binding commonly used today are shown in Fig. 10-8.

Most publications up to 96 pages (if on light-weight stock) are Saddle Stitched. Two or three staples are machine stitched through the "saddle" or fold in the center, Fig. 10-9. This is fast, economical, and

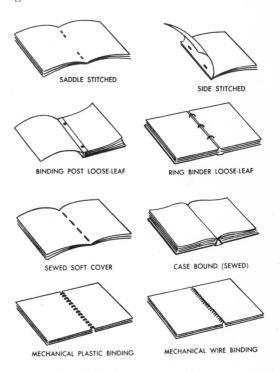

SADDLE STITCHED

SIDE STITCHED

BINDING POST LOOSE-LEAF

RING BINDER LOOSE-LEAF

SEWED SOFT COVER

CASE BOUND (SEWED)

MECHANICAL PLASTIC BINDING

MECHANICAL WIRE BINDING

Fig. 10-8. Basic types of binding.

Fig. 10-9. Saddle stitching, using a power-operated machine.

permits the pages to lie flat when opened. Covers of the same paper, or heavier cover stock may be used.

Magazines, inexpensive books, catalogs, etc. of more than 96 lightweight pages are frequently Side Stitched. A flexible paper cover is then glued to the back (backbone) of the printed sections.

For any book or catalog that needs the protection of hard covers, Case binding is desirable. In this more permanent type binding the sections are sewed together

Fig. 10-10. Applying cement to sheets in padding press.

then the hard cover is assembled and glued on.

Several variations of Mechanical Bindings are in use today. Made with metal, plastic, or wire, this type of binding permits the pages to lie perfectly flat when opened.

Another type of binding is Loose-Leaf Binding. In this type binding, sheets may be added and removed easily. The most common loose-leaf bindings are the binding-post and ring-binder types.

PADDING

Padding is the operation of putting a special adhesive on one edge of a stack of paper sheets to hold them together and

form a pad. The paper is jogged to make the ends square, a piece of chipboard is placed at the bottom of the pile, and the whole unit is placed in a padding press, Fig. 10-10.

OTHER BINDERY OPERATIONS

Other bindery operations include perforating, punching, drilling and wrapping. Perforating paper so it will tear easily is done on a machine called a perforator, or it can be done on a printing press.

BOOK BINDING IN THE SCHOOL SHOP

In this operation, we will learn how to sew the sheets together by hand, make end sheets, make a hard cover, and case the book in the cover.

The first step is to take between 10 to 15 sheets of 5-1/2 x 8-1/2 in. paper and hand

Fig. 10-11. Assembling or gathering folded sheets.

fold these sheets in half using a bone folder. This will give us folded sheets 4-1/4 x 5-1/2 in. These folded sheets are then gathered as in Fig. 10-11.

Step two is to prepare the end sheets. The end sheets should be made from special endsheet paper. Cut one end sheet the same length of the book; 5-1/2 in. The other way make it twice the width 4-1/4 + 4-1/4 or 8-1/2 + 1/2 in. This full size end sheet should be 5-1/2 x 9 in. Cut two end sheets from the end sheet stock, each the same size as a single sheet of your book pages 4-1/4 x 5-1/2 in. A piece of the cloth which is to be used in binding your book should be cut in a 2-in. wide strip, 5-1/2 in. long. This should then be glued to the two separate 4-1/4 x 5-1/2 in.

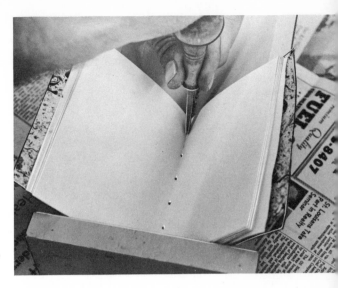

Fig. 10-14. *Using awl to punch holes for sewing.*

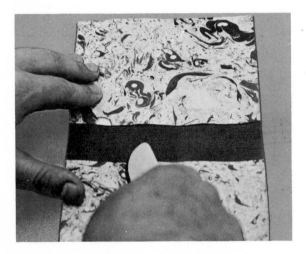

Fig. 10-12. *Gluing strip of cloth to end sheets. End sheets may be marbleized, or plain white paper.*

pieces, in the manner shown in Fig. 10-12. Be sure the finished side of the joint strip will be to the inside. The sheets overlap the joint.

Book-binders glue, or a suitable white paste may be used.

The next step is to fold each of the end

sheets in half and place them over the folded body sheets. The end sheets without the cloth strip go on first, then the end sheets with the cloth strip. The finished side of the cloth should be to the inside.

Take a V-trough such as shown in Fig. 10-13, and place the sheets in the trough up to the center fold. Mark off 1/2 in. from each end, and divide the remaining space into four equal spaces. Use a pencil to mark for five holes.

With an awl punch through each of the marked holes, Fig. 10-14.

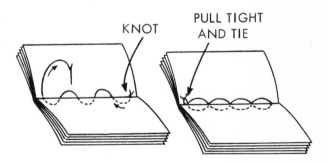

Fig. 10-15. *Sewing through book pages and end sheets.*

Fig. 10-13. *V-trough for holding folded sheets.*

Sew with a needle and a piece of linen or nylon binding thread as shown in Fig. 10-15. Tie a good knot. Next, apply a piece of backing flannel or super cloth. This piece should be about 3/4 in. wide, and 1/2 in. shorter than the length of the book. This is glued to the back of the book for strength, Fig. 10-16. Using a paper cutter trim the book on three sides.

Fig. 10-16. Adding super cloth (light-colored strip) to end sheet assembly.

To make the case or hard cover, cut two pieces of binders board (heavy chipboard type of material). These should be 1/4 in. longer than the book, or 5-1/2 + 1/4 in. and 1/8 in. narrower than the book or 4-1/4 - 1/8 in. or 4-1/8 in.

Obtain a piece of binding cloth that is 5-3/4 + 3/4 in. for each side or 7-1/4 in. one way, by twice the width of the book plus 3/4 in. for each side, or 10-3/4 in.

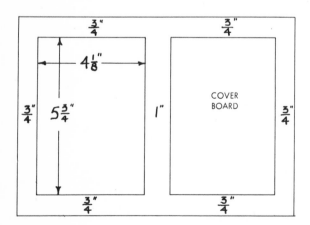

Fig. 10-17. Cover cloth layout showing where cover boards should be placed.

Mark off the back side of the binding cloth to show where the cover boards will go, Fig. 10-17. Glue the two boards into position. Put glue on the boards, and carefully place them on the cloth.

The corners are then clipped as shown in Fig. 10-18, leaving about 1/4 in. from the corner of the board to the edge of the

Fig. 10-18. Cloth cover after corners have been clipped.

cut. Glue one edge of the cloth that is over hanging. Be sure to use newspapers to keep the table and material clean. Turn the cloth over the edge of the board using a bone folder to get a neat job. Tuck in the corner as shown in Fig. 10-19. Then glue the next side down. This is called the nicked corner. Repeat this procedure to finish the case.

If the shop has a gold stamping machine,

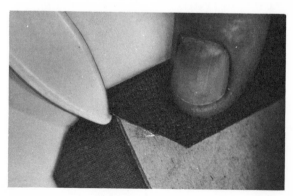

Fig. 10-19. Cover cloth being turned over corner of board.

Fig. 10-20. *Kwikprint stamping machine being used to stamp title on book.*

Fig. 10-22. *Gluing sewed book to cover, second step.*

set the type for the book title. After the glue has dried you are ready to stamp the title on the cloth cover, Fig. 10-20.

The final book binding operation is casing in the book. This is a bookbinders term for gluing the cover onto the sewed book. Place a sheet of waxed paper or newspaper between the end sheets. Open the top cover, and apply a light coating of glue to the end sheet, as shown in Fig. 10-21. Then, bring the cover to closed-book position, Fig. 10-22. Turn the book over and repeat the procedure for the second side of the book.

will take several hours. The completed book is shown in Fig. 10-24.

Fig. 10-23. *Book is being placed between metal plates with turned edges, to crease the binding at the hinges.*

Fig. 10-21. *Gluing sewed book to cover, first step.*

Crease the cloth binding at the hinges (near the back where the cover bends as the book is opened). Place the book between two heavy metal plates with turned edges, Fig. 10-23. Put this assembly in a press, under pressure, to dry. Drying

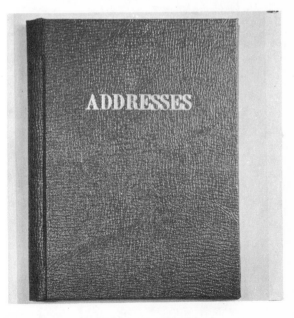

Fig. 10-24. *Completed book.*

FOLDING: Printed sheets are folded to make 8, 16, or 32 page sections.

ENDSHEETS of strong paper are tipped to first and last sections of book.

GATHERING: The sections are gathered in sequence to make a complete book.

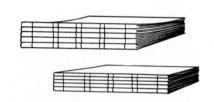

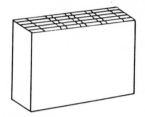

SEWING: The gathered sections are sewed together.

SMASHING: The sewed book is "smashed" to reduce bulk and swelling in the back.

BACK GLUING & TRIMMING: A plastic glue is applied to back and book is trimmed on three sides.

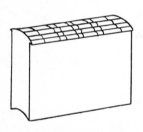

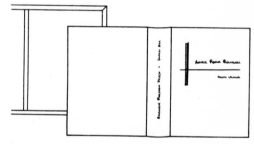

ROUNDING & BACKING: Backbone is rounded and backed to form the shape of the book.

SUPER & LINER: Muslin cloth and lining paper are glued to backbone and headbands are affixed.

CASEMAKING AND STAMPING: The case is made to fit the book and is stamped with cover and backbone design.

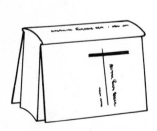

CASING IN: The book is pasted accurately and firmly into its case.

INSPECTION: The finished book is inspected for imperfections and the jacket is put on.

Fig. 10-25. Major steps in commercial book binding.
(John F. Cuneo Co.)

COMMERCIAL BOOK BINDING

For a graphic summary of the major steps involved in commercial book binding procedure, see Fig. 10-25.

ACTIVITY

PADDING

Information:

You have no doubt purchased pads of paper from a local store. In this assignment you will have an opportunity to make up a pad yourself and try this bindery operation. You may wish to use sheets such as printed in a previous activity.

Practical Work

Make roughs and layout for printing a job suitable for padding. Set type, and cut paper. Lock up and print about 150 copies. After printed sheets have dried, gather in bundles of about 50 sheets and put in chipboard backs. Put into padding press and apply padding compound.

PERFORATING AND STITCHING

Information:

This assignment will give you an opportunity to try out two finishing operations, perforating and stitching. One suggested project is a memo pad.

Practical Work

Make roughs and finished layout for printing a job suitable for perforating and stitching. Set type, cut paper, lock up and print about 150 copies. Gather in bundles of 50 sheets. Put on a chip board back, and a piece of cover stock on the front. Set stitcher for proper thickness and stitch.

BINDING A SADDLE-STITCHED BOOK

Information:

This will be a hard bound book when the assignment is completed, like a text book. Instead of binding blank sheets, plan for some printing on the sheets you will bind. One possible suggestion may be an address book. You could set your type and print each sheet in the book with a place of name, address and phone number. Another suggested idea is a gas mileage and trip book.

Practical Work

Make roughs and final layout of type to be set. The book should be planned for an individual page size of 4-1/4 x 5-1/2 in. This means the page before folding is 8-1/2 x 5-1/2 in. The book should have a total of 10 to 15 sheets before folding. Print job on both sides before hand folding of the sheets.

Cut paper for end sheets.

Fold printed sheets and proceed with the binding operations as outlined.

QUIZ - UNIT 10

1. Four operations that are performed in bindery are _____.
2. What safety precautions should be observed when operating a paper cutter?
3. In the school shop most paper folding is done by hand using a _____ folder.
4. In saddle stitching a publication, the staples are stitched through the fold in the center. True or false?
5. Padding is the operation of _____.
6. When binding a book in the school shop, what kind of thread should be used?
7. For what purpose is a V-trough used?

PHOTOGRAPHY

UNIT 11

1. Fundamentals of photography.

2. Film developing procedure.

3. Making contact prints and enlargements.

Photography and the printing processes are closely related to each other. Photography supplies not only a considerable part of the subject matter, but is also an essential part of the procedure necessary to produce the plates from which printed pieces are produced.

FUNDAMENTALS OF PHOTOGRAPHY

Photography may be defined as the art or process of producing images on sensitized surfaces by the action of light. The essentials required to take a picture are a camera, and some film (sensitized material).

Fig. 11-1, shows a drawing of a simple camera with the main parts identified.

CAMERA BODY: A light proof box with a device to hold the film at one end, and an opening for a lens at the other end.

LENS: A piece of glass in the front of the camera which is so shaped that it

changes the direction of the rays of light to form an image of the subject on the light-sensitive film from light reflected by the subject.

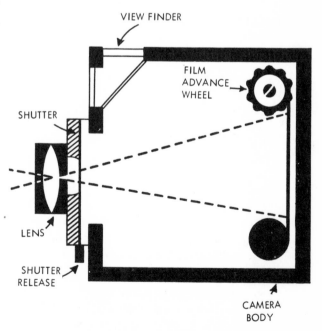

Fig. 11-1. Drawing which shows construction of a simple camera.

SHUTTER: A movable "curtain" that is ordinarily closed, but opens for a fraction of a second to allow light to enter through the lens, and affect the light-sensitive solution on the film.

SHUTTER RELEASE: A lever or plunger which trips a spring-activated shutter.

VIEW FINDER: A "peepsight" to show you what you will get in your picture.

FILM ADVANCE WHEEL: A device to move the film after each exposure so the camera will be ready to take another picture.

PHOTOGRAPHIC FILM

A film consists of a thin clear base (usually cellulose acetate) which is coated with light-sensitive emulsion. The emulsion is a thin layer of gelatin containing fine particles called silver halides.

The light sensitivity of the emulsion is due to the fact that the halides are affected by light. The action of light on the silver halides, however, is not visible until the emulsion is treated in a chemical solution called a Developer. The developing solution changes the silver halides affected by the light, to metallic silver. The amount of silver halides affected, and changed to metallic silver, is dependent upon the intensity and duration of the light striking the emulsion.

After development, there still remains in the emulsion, the unexposed silver halides (those not affected by light). These must be removed in order to make the image permanent. This is done by placing the film into another chemical solution called a Fixing Bath, or Hypo. The hypo clears the film and makes the unexposed silver halides soluble in water, but does not affect the metallic silver forming the visible image. The film is then washed to remove the unexposed silver which has been loosened, and the film is hung up to dry. The result of this procedure is to give you a negative or reverse image of the picture you took. The reason for the reversal in brightness is that bright objects reflect more light than dark objects, and affect more silver emulsion halides.

The negative is used to produce a positive print--a picture which shows the objects the way you see them.

DEVELOPING CAMERA FILM

Taking pictures with a camera is only half the fun; it is in the darkroom where the "real" photographic activity takes

Fig. 11-2. Film developing tank. Left, Disassembled tank. Right, Assembled tank.

place. We will discuss the steps necessary to develop a roll of film, make a contact print, and an enlargement.

Let's assume you have exposed (shot) all the pictures on the roll of film (panchromatic which is sensitive to all colors), have removed it from the camera, and are all set to proceed with the development of the film.

For the film development, we will use a roll-film developing tank, such as shown in Fig. 11-2. In examining the reel on

Fig. 11-3. Pouring developer into tank.

which the exposed film is to be wound, you will find it contains grooves into which the film is to be wound.

It is a good idea to cut a strip of paper, (such as heavy kraft wrapping) the width of your film, and practice feeding this into the reel. Start the paper at the outer edge of the reel and feed the film into the grooves until the entire film is on the reel. To remove the film from the reel the procedure is reversed. Winding and unwinding the film from the reel is easy, once you get the knack of doing it.

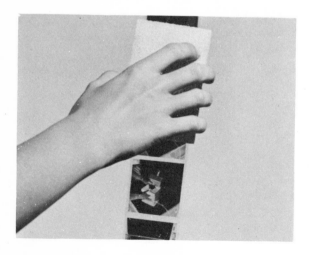

Fig. 11-4. Using sponge to remove excess moisture from developed film.

DEVELOPING ROLL FILM

Since the film being used is sensitive to all light, it will be necessary to load the film into the developing tank in total darkness. Unroll the film from the film spool, and separate the film from the paper. Feed the film into the grooves of the film reel as you did the sheet of paper when practicing. After the tank is loaded and the cover is on securely, all other developing operations may be carried out in a lighted room.

Use the type developer, at the temperature recommended by the manufacturer of your film. In school shops ready-mixed stock solutions are usually available. Use the quantity of developer specified by the manufacturer of the developing tank. On some developing tanks there is a capacity chart right on the cover of the tank.

Pour the developer into the tank through opening at edge of the cover, Fig. 11-3. Rotate the reel counterclockwise a few times to vigorously agitate the film and assure even wetting of the emulsion. Agitate for 5 seconds at 30-second intervals during development. Leave the film in the developer for length of time specified by the directions supplied with the developer.

When the development of the film is complete, tip the tank and pour the developer out. Rinse the film by pouring in Stop Bath, or water at 65 to 75 deg. F., for length of time specified by manufacturer of film.

Pour out stop bath solution, and pour in the Fixing Bath, or Hypo. Fix 5 to 10 minutes, with occasional agitation. As soon as the fixing of the film has been completed the cover may be removed from the film developing tank. Wash the film for 20 to 30 min. by placing the tank minus the cover in a sink under a tap. A sponge is used to remove excess water, Fig. 11-4, and the film is hung up to dry.

MAKING CONTACT PRINTS

After the film negative has been processed, the next step is to make a positive image or print from the negative. A print

Fig. 11-5. Contact printing with printing box. Left, Placing negative and paper in place. Right, Making print.

is made on paper coated with an emulsion similar to the emulsion on film.

A contact print may be made using a Printing Box, Fig. 11-5, or a Printing Frame, Fig. 11-6. The print is called a contact print because the negative and the

Fig. 11-6. Making contact print with printing frame. Both sides of frame are shown.

printing paper are held in direct contact, emulsion to emulsion. Light is passed through the negative to the printing paper, resulting in the formation of a positive or reversed image in the emulsion of the paper. See Fig. 11-7. The image on the print is made visible by processing it in a developing solution made for photographic paper.

Fig. 11-7. Above, Negative print. Below, Positive print.

The developing is done in trays, Fig. 11-8. You will need a developer to make the print, a short stop to stop development, and hypo or fix to fix the print so it will be permanent. Photo prints are made in a darkroom, using a safelight.

Time required for developing, short stop, and fixing will vary according to the manufacturer's product being used, but the approximate times are: developer 45 to 60 seconds, short stop 30 seconds, and fixer

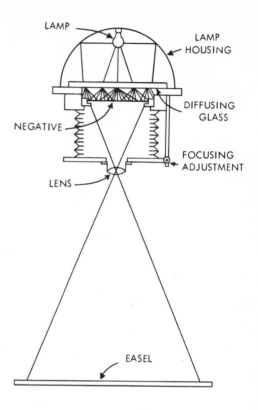

Fig. 11-8. Developing photo prints. Three trays are needed--one for Developer, one for Short Stop Bath, and one for Hypo Fixer.

5 to 10 minutes. After the prints have been removed from the hypo, they should be washed in running water for 35 to 45 minutes.

Fig. 11-10. Drawing which shows how a photo enlarger is constructed and works.

To dry the prints they may be placed between blotters, dried in a regular print dryer, or placed on highly polished metal sheets, called Ferrotype plates, Fig. 11-9. Prints dried on a ferrotype plate have a high gloss finish.

Fig. 11-9. Placing photo print on ferrotype plate.

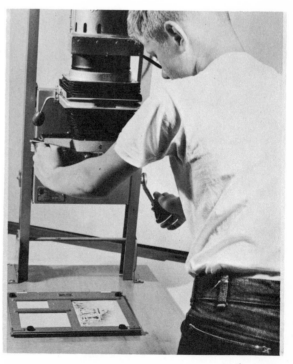

Fig. 11-11. Using a photo enlarger in a school shop.

Fig. 11-12. An enlargement and a contact print, made from the same negative.

MAKING AN ENLARGEMENT

Because many cameras used today make miniature pictures (when contact prints are made), most people like to make enlargements (large prints) of the pictures they like best. In making a large print from a small negative, we will need an enlarger or projection printer. In projection printing, Fig. 11-10, and 11-11, the negative is separated from the paper and the negative image is projected by means of a lens, onto the sensitized paper.

In making enlargements, the sensitized paper is developed the same way as a contact print. See Fig. 11-12.

ACTIVITY

MAKING PRINTS, ENLARGEMENTS

Information

This assignment will cover quite a few of the operations involved in photography: shooting or exposing a roll of film, developing that roll of film, making contact prints, and enlargements of several of the prints. When you are taking the pictures it will be best if you photograph several different kinds of subjects: Landscapes, buildings, groups of people, a portrait, pets, etc. If you have a flash attachment, an indoor flash picture should be included.

Practical Work

1. Expose roll of film.
2. Develop roll of film (use manufacturer's recommendations as to time and temperature).
3. Dry film.
4. Make contact prints of each of the pictures.
5. Choose three best pictures and make 5 x 7 enlargements.
6. Mount your favorite picture.

QUIZ - UNIT 11

1. Photography may be defined as _____.
2. What is the purpose of the camera lens?
3. Light sensitivity of film is due to the fact that the ____ it contains are affected by ____.
4. Is it possible to see the picture on exposed film before it is developed?
5. What is the function of Hypo?
6. Panchromatic film is sensitive to all colors except blue. True or false?
7. In using a tank developer, when may we turn on the light?
8. A contact print is so-called because _____.
9. Do prints dried on a ferrotype plate have a dull or a glossy surface?

MATHEMATICS FOR PRINTERS

UNIT 12

1. Printers' systems of measurement.
2. Measuring type.
3. Cutting paper.
4. Figuring paper costs.

In order to complete many of the operations in a print shop, it is necessary to know, and to be able to use, the printer's system of measurement.

In this Unit, we will review some of the items discussed previously, and learn more about solving printers' math problems.

The Point system of type measurement has two basic units. The first is the Point. This measures about 1/72 in. The point is actually just short of 1/72 in. but for all practical purposes it is considered to be 1/72 in.

The next unit of measurement is the Pica. This unit consists of 12 points. Six picas are considered to be equal to 1 in., Fig. 12-1.

In discussing type size, printers speak of point size. In discussing type forms, or

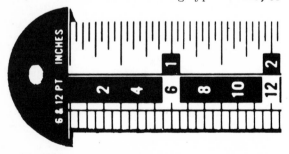

Fig. 12-1. Line gauge used by printers. Note that 6 picas equal 1 inch.

assembled type, they refer to the width and depth of the form as so many picas wide and deep.

ADDITION PROBLEM

Add 15 picas and 3 points, 9 picas and 8 points, and 5 picas 6 points.

Picas	Points
15	3
9	8
5	6
29 picas	17 points
+ 1	− 12 (12 points = one pica)

Answer 30 picas 5 points

SUBTRACTION PROBLEM

Subtract 15 picas 7 points from 30 picas 10 points.

Picas	Points
30	10
− 15	7

Answer 15 picas 3 points

MULTIPLICATION PROBLEM

Multiply 6 picas 5 points by 4 picas 3 points.

Picas Points   Picas Points
  6   5 = 6 5/12   x 4   3 = 4 3/12
6 5/12 x 4 3/12 = 77/12 x 51/12 = 3927 =
                                   ———
                                   144
27 39/144

CHANGING FRACTIONS TO POINTS PROBLEM

39/144 x 12/1 = 39/12 = 3 3/12

Answer to problem 27 picas 3 points

DIVISION PROBLEM

Divide 30 picas 6 points by 5 picas 2 points.

Picas	Points		Picas	Points
30	6 = 30 6/12		5	2 = 5 2/12

30 6/12 divide 5 2/12

$$\frac{366}{12} \div \frac{62}{12}$$

$$\frac{366}{12} \times \frac{12}{62} = \frac{366}{62} = 5\ 56/62$$

CHANGING FRACTIONS TO POINTS PROBLEM

$$\frac{56}{62} \times \frac{12}{1} = \frac{672}{62} = 10\ 52/62\ \text{or}\ 11\ \text{points}$$

Answer 5 picas 11 points

Most print shops have line gauges that measure picas and half picas on one side, and on the other edge they measure inches and fraction of an inch.

Besides knowing how to do the basic operation of arithmetic with picas and points, a printer should also know how to change inches to picas and points and picas, to inches.

To change inches to picas, multiply inches by 6. To change inches to points multiply inches by 72.

To change picas to points multiply picas by 12.

To change picas to inches, divide picas by 6.

To change points to picas, divide points by 12.

To change points to inches, divide points by 72.

PROBLEMS TO BE SOLVED

1. A newspaper has 6 columns, each 11 picas, with a 6-point rule between each column. The margins on each side are 3 picas. How wide is the paper in inches?
2. A job is 30 picas wide. A cut 2-1/2 in. is placed in one corner of the job. How wide would the type lines be at the side of the cut?
3. How wide is the type page if it has 12 columns, each 12 picas 4 points? (No space between columns).
4. The depth of some copy is 2-3/4 in. Give its depth in picas and points.
5. A line of type measures 25 picas. Give its length both in inches and in points.
6. Five leads are needed for a form that is 36 picas wide. How many inches of leading are necessary?
7. How many em quads of 6 point type would fit into an em quad of 72 points?
8. Add 10 points, 8 picas 6 points, 24 picas, 5 inches and 169 points.
9. A job is printed on a piece of paper measuring 9-1/2 by 14 in. The right margin measures 198 points. The left margin measures 8 picas. The top margin measures 16 picas and the bottom margin measures 204 points. Find the size of the type form in picas.

CUTTING PAPER

Another important calculation that a printer frequently has to make, is how to cut paper to prevent waste.

Paper is purchased in standard sized sheets from a paper dealer. The printer then has to cut this paper to the size necessary for the job to be run on the press.

The method used to figure the number of press size sheets that can be cut from a stock size sheet is a matter of division. The basic formula for this can be stated this way:

$$\frac{\text{Dimensions of stock sheet}}{\text{Dimensions of press sheet}} = \text{pieces cut}$$

PROBLEM: How many 3 in. x 5 in. press size sheets can be cut from a stock size sheet 17 in. x 22 in.? Figure this problem vertical first.

17 x 22   3 into 17 = 5 times
3 x 5   5 into 22 = 4 times
5 x 4 = 20

This shows you can get 20 press size sheets. Now repeat this same problem, but figure it criss-cross this time.

17 x 22   3 into 22 = 7 times
3 x 5   5 into 17 = 3 times
7 x 3 = 21

When figured this way you can get 21 pieces of press-size stock, from each 17 x 22 in. sheet. In solving this problem the correct way to cut would be the second method. Before actually cutting the stock to size you should make a "cutting chart." This shows where the cuts are to be made, Fig. 12-2. Then you will need to decide the order in which the cuts are to be made. See Fig. 12-3.

In the layouts, the areas with the wavy lines represent the scrap or waste stock.

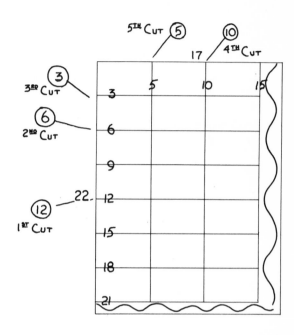

Fig. 12-3. Printer's layout which shows order in which cuts indicated in Fig. 12-2, are to be made.

This is sometimes usable as we will see in solving the next problem.

PROBLEMS: How many 3 x 5 in. press-size sheets can be cut from a stock size sheet 17 x 28 in.?

Follow the same procedure as we did in the previous problem. Work the problem vertically and criss-cross.

17 x 28   17 x 28
3 x 5   3 x 5
5 x 5 = 25   9 x 3 = 27

As we look at the answers in this problem, the criss-cross method looks best. Let's look at the vertical method, and check the size of the scrap or usable waste. Where 5 in. is divided into 28 in., it goes 5 times, giving us 25 in. with a 3 in. strip 17 in. long left over. Our press size

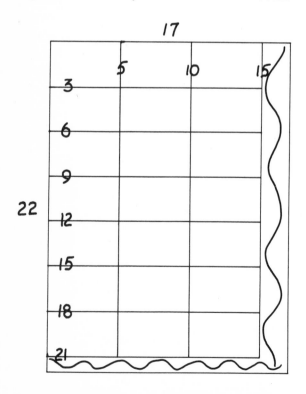

Fig. 12-2. A printer's layout showing how 17 x 22 in. stock is to be cut into 3 x 5 sheets.

sheet is 3 x 5 in. This will go into 3 x 17 figured vertically:

$$\begin{array}{c} 3 \times 17 \\ \underline{3 \times 5} \\ 1 \times 3 = 3 \end{array}$$

When we add the three sheets to the 25 sheets we obtain by the previous figuring we will have 28 press-size sheets.

$$\begin{array}{cc} \dfrac{17 \times 28}{3 \times 5} & \dfrac{3 \times 17}{3 \times 5} \\ 5 \times 5 = 25 & 1 \times 3 = 3 \\ \underline{+ \quad 3} & \\ 28 & \end{array}$$

From this you can see that it is important to check the usable waste when figuring how paper is to be cut. We now proceed to draw our cutting plan, as in Fig. 12-4.

Be sure to indicate the order in which the cuts are to be made. In this case the first cut must be to cut off the usable scrap.

This is put aside and you proceed to make all the other cuts on the main stock. Then, you cut the piece you have set aside.

If you have a problem that has fractions such as a sheet of paper for the press measuring 3-1/2 x 5-1/2 in., remember that you must cut each piece 3-1/2 x 5-1/2 in. Example of this is shown here.

PROBLEMS: How many 3-1/2 x 5-1/2 in. pieces can be cut from stock 17 x 22 in. in size?

$$\begin{array}{cc} 17 \times 22 & 17 \times 22 \\ \underline{3\text{-}1/2 \times 5\text{-}1/2} & \underline{3\text{-}1/2 \times 5\text{-}1/2} \\ 4 \times 4 = 16 & 6 \times 3 = 18 \end{array}$$

You can see the criss-cross way is best. Now make a cutting chart. You will see how different it is from the problem when the measurements were 3 x 5 in., Fig. 12-5.

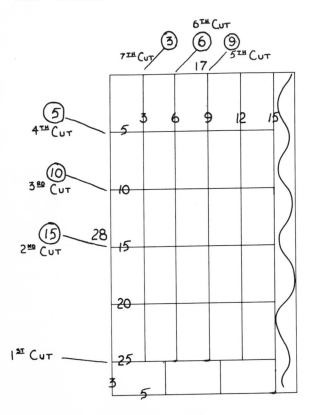

Fig. 12-4. *Getting maximum number of 3 x 5 sheets from 17 x 28 stock.*

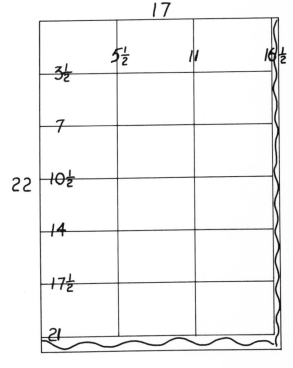

Fig. 12-5. *Layout for cutting 17 x 22 sheets into 3½ x 5½ in. sheets.*

FIGURING QUANTITY OF PAPER NEEDED

The next problem is how many stock sheets it will take to do the job.

Let's take our original problem and work from that point.

PROBLEMS: How many 3 x 5 press size sheets can be cut from a stock size sheet 17 x 22? Then, how many stock size sheets will be required to print 250 copies?

We already know that we can get 21 press size sheets from each stock sheet. We now divide the number of sheets required by the number of press sheets we can get from each stock sheet.

$$\begin{array}{r} \underline{19} \\ 11\ \overline{21}\quad \text{or 12 sheets} \\ 21\overline{)250} \\ \underline{21} \\ 40 \\ \underline{21} \\ 19 \end{array}$$

We see it will take 12 17 x 22 sheets.

ALLOWING FOR SPOILAGE

In cutting paper, printing, and binding, some sheets will certainly be spoiled. For this reason, it is necessary when figuring out how much paper will be needed for a particular job, to make an allowance for this spoilage.

The percentage of spoiled sheets will vary according to the quantity of sheets to be printed, how many colors, weight of stock, kind of press used, and type of folding and binding.

You may be interested in knowing that in obtaining paper for this book, which is printed in one color ink, we allowed 6 per cent for spoilage in printing and binding.

PAPER GRAIN

In commercial shops on jobs where the paper stock must be folded neatly, another consideration is the grain direction (direction in which the majority of the fibers lay).

All papers have a definite grain. A job should ordinarily be planned so the folds are made with the grain.

PROBLEMS

Be sure to draw the cutting layout. Do not include extra stock for spoilage.

1. How many press size sheets 3 x 5 in. can be cut from a stock sheet 38 x 50 in.?
2. A job requires 250 sheets 6 x 9 in. cut from stock 25 x 38 in. How many stock sheets will be required?
3. How many 6-1/4 x 9-1/2 in. pieces can be cut from a stock sheet 26 x 40 in.?
4. From one stock sheet 19 x 28 in. how many 2-1/2 x 4-1/2 in. pieces can be cut?
5. A job requires 500 sheets 4-1/2 x 3-3/4 in. The stock sheet measures 25-1/2 x 30-1/2 in. How many are required?
6. How many 2-1/2 x 4-1/2 in. pieces can be cut from 25-1/2 x 30-1/2 in. stock?
7. 275 sheets, 5 x 7 in. are needed for a job. These are to be cut from stock 19 x 24 in. How many stock sheets are required?
8. How many 8 x 10 in. pieces can be cut from 20 x 26 in. stock?
9. How many 17 x 22 in. stock sheets will be needed for 1200 letterheads, 8-1/2 x 11 in. in size?
10. 300 press sheets are to be cut 3 x 8 in. out of 28 x 34 in. stock. How many stock sheets are required?

FIGURING COST OF PAPER

We have found out how to figure paper quantity. Now, let's look into the method used to figure paper costs. Most papers such as book, offset, bonds, etc., are sold by the pound. They are listed in the paper catalog by the price per hundred weight (cwt.).

Because paper is usually sold by the pound, we should become familiar with the way paper weight is designated. Paper is listed for example as Bond 17 x 22 - 20. The dash number following the paper size indicates the weights per ream (500 sheets). Some papers may be listed as Bond 17 x 22 - 40 M. Here the M shows that the weight shown is for 1000 sheets, instead of 500 sheets.

the Unit on Paper and Ink. Let's see how to use the paper cost figures given in Fig. 12-6.

PROBLEMS

Find the cost of 25 stock sheets 17 x 22 in. - 20 Bond at $25.25 per cwt.

Formula:

$$\frac{\text{Number of stock sheets} \times \text{twice ream wt.}}{1000} =$$

weight of the number of sheets

$$\frac{25 \times 40}{1000} = 1 \text{ or 1 pound of paper}$$

Now to find the cost by multiplying the weight of the sheets by the cost per pound. The price per cwt. can be changed to the

BOND	Price Per Cwt		4	16	Broken
Everyday Bond White	Ream $33.00	Carton $23.50	Cartons $20.75	Cartons $19.20	Ream $49.00

Fig. 12-6. Example of prices charged for Bond paper.

Were you to examine a paper catalog, and turn to the section on Bond paper for example, the prices might appear as shown in Fig. 12-6.

The price varies according to the amount of paper the printer buys. A broken ream is less than 500 sheets; a ream or package as it is sometimes listed, 500 sheets; carton nearest even number of reams to about 125 pounds.

You can see that the big user of paper is able to buy at a definite advantage.

The prices listed here are of course ficticious but the savings are about in that proportion. Each different brand, and each of the many kinds of paper available has a separate price schedule.

It would be well to review the information given on kinds of paper and sizes, in

cost per pound by just moving the decimal point two places to the left.

25.25 per cwt. = .2525 per pound

$$\begin{array}{r} .2525 \\ \times\ 1 \\ \hline .2525 \end{array} = \text{the cost of one pound of the}$$
above paper

BRISTOLS

The cost of bristols or card stock is figured in another manner. This is usually priced by C sheets (This means per 100 sheets).

PROBLEM

Find the cost of 10 sheets of 25-1/2 by 30-1/2 white index bristol, using the price shown in Fig. 12-7. We would have to pay at the rate of $7.30 per C sheets, as 10 is less than 100 sheets. To find the cost per

BRISTOL	Price per 100 Sheets		4	Broken
90 lb.	Package	Carton	Cartons	Package
	$6.50	$3.95	$3.35	$7.30

Fig. 12-7. Example of bristol stock prices.

sheet, move the decimal two places to the left. This will be the price per sheet.

$$10 \times .073 = .73$$

In solving this type problem, the formula would be number of sheets, times price per sheet = cost.

ENVELOPES

Envelopes are another item that printers use a great deal. These also come in many sizes and many prices. Three common sizes used are the #6-3/4 (size 3-5/8 x 6-1/2 in.), the monarch size (size 3-7/8 x 7-1/2 in.), and the #10 size (4-1/8 x 9-1/2 in.).

Envelopes are priced different than paper and cardboard. See Fig. 12-8.

The M per carton means the quantity in thousands of envelopes per carton.

Figuring envelope cost goes like this:

PROBLEM

Find the cost of 750 # 6-3/4 - 20 envelopes (using cost figures shown in Fig. 12-8). Formula: number of envelopes times price per envelope = cost.

To find the cost per envelope when they are priced per 1000, you move the decimal point three places to the left.

$$750 \times .00456 = \$3.42$$

PAPER PRICED BY 1000 SHEETS

Another pricing procedure used by paper companies is to list prices by the 1000 or M sheets. This pricing method includes all kinds of paper, bristols, blotting, and would be just like envelopes are priced now.

A typical column from a Bond paper page would appear as in Fig. 12-9.

ENVELOPES	Substance Weight	M envelopes per carton	1-4 Cartons	5-9 Cartons	10 Cartons	Bkn. Carton
6 3/4	20	5	$3.71	$3.33	$2.99	$4.56

Fig. 12-8. Price of 6 3/4 size envelopes.

BOND	M sheets weight	sheets per carton	16 carton	4 carton	1 carton	500 sheets	bkn. pkg.
Everyday Bond				price per M sheets			
Finish-Regular Prints-Offset Letterpress							
Basis 17x22 - 20	40	3000	9.36	10.06	11.32	13.22	21.02

Fig. 12-9. Bond paper priced by the 1000 sheets.

OCCUPATIONAL OPPORTUNITIES

1. Jobs in all parts of country.

2. How to enter field.

3. Educational requirements.

The printing crafts provide employment for many thousands of skilled workers. These trades offer especially good opportunities for young men willing to spend the time required to learn a skilled craft. Skilled printing workers generally have year-round employment at much better than average earnings.

Jobs in the graphic arts field are to be found throughout the country, in small towns as well as big cities. Some printing craftsmen also have opportunities to go into business for themselves.

Today, training for jobs in graphic arts is usually specialized--the training is directed to a specific area such as type composition, photography, platemaking, or presswork. Moreover, training is largely confined to one of the basic printing methods--letterpress, gravure, lithography, or silk screen.

In addition to skilled craftsmen, printing establishments employ a great many persons as estimators, salesmen, accountants, engineers, stenographers, clerks, and laborers of various types. Newspapers and other publishers employ reporters and editors.

The most common way of entering a skilled printing occupation is through apprenticeship. In some of the smaller shops, it is possible to pick up the printing trades by working with printing craftsmen, or by a combination of work experience and schooling.

Printing apprenticeship usually lasts from 4 to 6 years, depending on the occupation and the shop or area practices. The training program covers all phases of the particular trade and usually includes classroom study in related technical subjects in addition to training on the job. To be eligible for apprenticeship, applicants are generally required to be between 18 and 30 years of age.

In selecting applicants for apprenticeship most employers require a high school education, or its equivalent. A thorough knowledge of spelling, punctuation, and grammar is essential for some of the trades. Courses in art, such as drawing, design, color, and lettering, as well as courses in physics and chemistry, are also helpful for many kinds of printing work.

A continued rise in the volume of printing material produced is anticipated because of population growth, the expansion of the economy, and the trend toward greater use of attractively printed material for packaging, information, advertising, and various other industrial and commercial purposes.

The Graphic Arts field offers great opportunities for ambitious, capable workers.

DICTIONARY OF TERMS
(Printers Lingo)

UNIT 14

AD COPY: Copy for a advertisement.

AGAINST THE GRAIN: Opposite to or against the direction to which the fibers run in a sheet of paper.

ALBUMEN PLATE: Plate used in lithography coated with bichromated egg sensitizing solution.

ALIVE: A printer's term applied to a form of type after it has been set, and until it is ready to be distributed.

AMALGAMATED LITHOGRAPHERS OF AMERICA: A trade union of journeymen lithographers.

AMPERSAND· Name for the character &.

ANTIQUE FINISH: A term applied to paper that has not been calendered. It is practically unfinished, and possesses a rough, soft, uneven surface, known as low finish.

APPRENTICE: One who has not completed the required term of course of instruction in a printing plant necessary to become a journeyman, under trade organization rule.

ARABIC NUMERAL: Any of the ten figures, 1 - 10.

ASCENDER: Part of a tall lower-case letter which extends above the body.

ASPHALTUM: A tar-like material that protects a plate against acid and corrosion.

AUTOMATIC FEEDER: A mechanical contrivance for feeding sheets of paper at regular intervals, into a printing press.

BACK EDGE: Rear edge of press sheet as it goes through the press.

BACK UP: To print on back side of already-printed sheet.

BAIL: On a platen press, either of the metal bands hinged on the upper and lower edges of the platen which serve to hold the sheets of the tympan in place.

BASIC WEIGHT: As applied to paper, the weight of a sheet of paper in terms of its weight in a full ream in the size represented by its class.

BEARER: A term used by printers for various devices which serve the general end of protecting the type in a form.

BED: The flat metal part of a printing press on which the form is laid.

BEN DAY: A process for providing a shaded background.

BIBLE PAPER: A thin, opaque book paper, possessing strength and durability, and suitable for printing Bibles.

BINDER'S BOARD: A tough, hard, smooth fiber board used by book binders for covers.

BINDING: The cover or fastenings of a book.

BLANK: A quad, slug, piece of furniture or other material used in a type form to make a blank space on the printed page or sheet.

BLANKET: Sheet of rubber, reinforced with fabric, which is clamped around offset cylinder, and transfers ink from the printing plate to the paper.

BLEED: Term applied to printed sheets where image is flush with the edge of paper.

BLOCKING OUT: Eliminating undesirable portions of copy or illustrations.

BOND: A general name given to a kind of paper of hard, tough texture.

BOND INK: An ink used in letterpress printing for writing on highly-sized paper.

BONE FOLDER: A piece of flat, smooth bone with rounded ends, from five to eight inches long, used to fold sheets by hand.

BOOK CLOTH: A woven material, pressed and embossed in many finishes, and made in numerous colors, shades and designs, used in binding books.

BRAYER: A small hand roller used to spread ink on the inking table, or to apply it to the distributing plates or rollers of a press.

BURIN: An engraver's tool with an oblique point of tempered steel, used in line engraving.

BY-LINE: A name given to the line over or under a signed article in a newspaper which tells the name of the writer.

CALENDER: A term descriptive of a high-surfaced paper procured by passing paper between calender rolls.

CALIFORNIA JOB CASE: Type case which contains complete font of type used for hand composition, arranged in a particular manner.

CAP: A printer's term for capital or capitalize.

CAPITAL LETTER: Any of the large letters, of a font of type or of an alphabet.

CARDBOARD: A stiff, compact pasteboard made in various qualities and thicknesses, and used for numerous purposes in printing.

CASE: A shallow try or receptacle for holding type, and from which the compositor works.

CASE BOUND: Book bound in stiff board cover.

CASEIN: An albuminous substance obtained from milk and vegetable matter, used in paper making as a size for and as a paste for coated papers.

CATHODE: The negative pole in the apparatus for plating of electrotypes and steel dies.

CHASE: (letterpress printing) A metal frame in which type forms are locked ready for the press.

CHINA CLAY: A very fine white clay used in paper making for loading and coating paper.

CHIPPER: Machine with rotating knives which cuts pulpwood logs to chips about 1 in. square and 1/8 in. thick.

COATED PAPER: Paper which has a surface coating, giving it a smooth and usually a glossy finish.

COBALT DRIER: An ingredient added to ink causing it to dry.

COLD COLORS: Colors on the blue side of the spectrum.

COLD-SET INK: An ink that reverses the drying process on the paper, by using cold instead of heat to change the ink from a fluid to a solid state.

COLD TYPE: Type set where no hot metal is necessary.

COLLATE: In bookbinding, to examine the signatures for a book to ascertain whether they are correct and follow in proper order.

COLOR PROOFS: Proof of illustration or type pulled in color.

COMBINATION PLATE: A printing plate consisting of two kinds of engravings, usually a line and a halftone, combined into one plate.

COMPOSITION: The process of setting and arranging type for printing.

COMPOSITION ROLLER: A cylinder consisting of a metal core coated with a flexible composition made from a mixture of glue, molasses, glycerine and other materials, and used for inking type forms on printing presses.

CONTRAST: Comparison of tonal highlights and shadows.

COPPER ENGRAVING: The art or process of engraving or etching a design on copper plates, or the taking of impressions or prints from copper plates.

COPPER ETCHING: A printing plate reproducing a line drawing, made on copper instead of on zinc.

COPY: Manuscript or text furnished to printer.

CORNER MARKS: Lines or marks indicating extreme edges of job.

COVER: In printing, the outer leaves of bound or stitched booklets, magazines or similar works.

CUT: Type-high plate used for printing an illustration.

DANDY ROLLER: In papermaking, a roll with a raised design used to form a watermark in the paper.

DEAD FORM: A form of type matter that has been used and that is ready for distribution.

DESCENDER: Part of lower-case letter that projects below normal body line.

DIECUT: To cut paper, cardboard, etc., to a desired shape by means of a steel die on a printing press.

DIRTY PROOF: A proof that contains many errors or typographical imperfections.

DISTRIBUTION: The act of separating type which has been used, and returning the characters and materials to their proper receptacles.

DOCTOR BLADE: A round edge steel knife, used in rotogravure printing for wiping off surplus ink from the surface of the cylinder, just before the impression is taken on the sheet.

DOT: In halftones, the individual element of a screened printing plate.

DRAWSHEET: The top sheet of the tympan on a printing press, and the one to which guides are attached.

DRIER: A substance added to printing ink to insure quick and proper drying.

DUMMY: A set of sheets or leaves made up to show in advance, size, shape and form of the printed job.

EDGE GILDING: Putting gold leaf on the edge of a book.

EDGE MARBLEIZING: Marbleizing the edge of a book.

EGGSHELL: A paper having a surface similar to that of an eggshell.

ELECTROTYPE: A facsimile plate of a type form or another plate, produced by taking an impression in wax, depositing in this mold a thin shell of copper or other metal by an electroplating process, and backing with type metal.

EM: The square of the body of type, used as a unit of measurement for type matter.

EMBOSS: To produce a design or lettering in relief upon a plane surface, such as paper in printing or engraving, or leather in bookbinding.

ENAMEL FINISH: A finish on paper produced by coating it with a mixture of China clay, satin white and casein, either glossy or dull.

END SHEET: An extra sheet of paper, either plain or printed with a decorative design, placed between the cover and the body of a book.

ENGRAVING: The art or process of producing a design, by incision or corrosion, upon the surface of blocks of wood or plates of metal. A halftone or line plate.

EN: A unit of measurement for type matter, being the same depth and one-half the breadth of an em in a body of type.

ESTIMATE: The approximate cost of a certain job of printing.

ETCHING SOLUTION: A chemical used to eat away the metal in the plate making process.

EVAPORATION: To pass off in vapor, as a fluid, to escape as vapor or in the manner of vapor.

EXPOSURE: Photographic term for period of time during which a light-sensitive surface is exposed to light either in a camera or printing frame.

FACE: The part of a type character that appears in relief on the printing end of the type, and which produces the impression in printing.

FAMILY: The complete group or collection of all the sizes and styles of type of the same design.

FEEDER: One who feeds paper into a printing press or ruling machine, or the device on automatically-fed machines performing the same function.

FELT SIDE: The smooth side of a sheet of paper.

FINISHER: In bookbinding, one who receives a volume after it has been sewed, and who puts it in its cover and adds the ornamentation and final touches to make it complete.

FLAT: (lithography) Assembly of photographic negatives or positives in position on goldenrod paper, glass or vinyl acetate for exposure in vacuum frame in contact with sensitized metal pressplate.

FLAT: Monotonous in hue, shade and color; free from gloss.

FLAT BED PRESS: Any press which prints from a flat, plane form.

FOCUS: Point at which light passing through lenses of a camera converge on photographic film plate or ground glass to form a sharp image of original.

FOLDING: To lap or lay one part of a sheet of paper over another.

FOLIO: Page number.

FONT: A complete assortment of type of one size and style, including all letters of the alphabet, both large and small, points, accents, figures, etc.

FOOT MARGIN: The blank space at the foot or bottom of a page; tail margin.

FOTOSETTER: A machine designed to set type on a film.

FOUNDRY: The section of a printing plant or stereotyping house where matrices are made from type forms and plates and stereotypes are cast.

FOUNDRY CHASE: A chase made especially to hold forms for electrotyping and stereotyping.

FOUNTAIN: A reservoir or receptacle for ink or water on a printing press.

FOUR COLOR PROCESS: Printing process in which all colors may be produced by using primary colors - red, yellow and blue, with the addition of black.

FURNITURE: Blocks of wood which are used for locking type forms and filling blank spaces in forms.

GALLEY: Flat metal tray in which type is placed after it is set.

GANGING: Various printing jobs are combined and run together on the same sheet and are separated later by cutting.

GATHER: To arrange sheets or signatures in proper order.

GAUGE PIN: A pin or piece of stamped sheet metal, used on the tympan of a platen press as a paper guide.

GOLDENROD FLAT: Method of assembling lithographic negatives into a complete page or plate layout form. Goldenrod paper is ruled to desired layout, window openings are cut to fit the work and negatives are fastened into position.

GRADATION: In photographic originals and prints, the range of tones from the brightest highlights to the deepest shadows.

GRAINED PLATE: In lithography, a plate having an abraded or roughened surface which gives it the quality of being able to retain water while printing.

GRAPHITE: A fine dust made from carbon, used as a release in electrotyping.

GRIPPER EDGE: Edge of sheet which is fed into press gripper.

GRIPPERS: Metal fingers that clasp the paper and draw it through the press.

GUMMING UP: Applying solution of gum arabic to lithographic plate to prevent oxidation of non-printing area, and to protect it during washout operations.

GUTENBERG: The man given credit for the invention of movable metal type.

HAIR LINE: A term designating type having unusually thin lines on its face.

HALFTONE: Photomechanical printing surface and impression made from this surface in which detail and tone values are shown by using a series of evenly spaced dots of varying size and shape. The dot area varies in direct proportion to the intensity of tones they represent.

HAND PROOF: Proof of a printing plate where inking of plate is done by hand, and proof is made by hand, on a hand or motor-driven proof press.

HEADBAND: A thin metal slip at the top of the tympan of a prnting press. Also, a decorative strip placed at both ends of a bound book.

HEAD: The top line of a page, or an inscription at the top of a page or section of a book or manuscript.

HOT TYPE: Type cast from molten metal.

IMPOSING STONE: The stone on which compositors impose type matter and lock it up in chases ready for printing.

IMPRESSION CYLINDER: The cylinder on a printing press which carries the packing and make-ready, and which produces the impression.

IMPRESSION: In printing, the inked image printed on paper as it runs through the press.

IMPRINT: The name or trademark of the printer or publisher, sometimes with the date and place of issue, printed on a book or other printed matter.

INTAGLIO PRINTING: Printing that is done from plates in which the design or lettering is etched below the surface of the plate.

INTERTYPE: Trade name of a slug-casting machine similar in principle and operation to the Linotype.

ITALIC: Type that slants to the right.

JOB INK: Ink used on job-presses.

JOB PRINTING: The type of work done in small commercial establishments.

JOG: Straighten a pile of sheets of paper.

KERN: That part of the type face which projects beyond the body or shank.

KEY: Register marks used as guides when aligning further work on other operations.

KRAFT: A tough, strong, natural colored paper.

LACQUER FILM: Lacquer-coated film used in making silk-screen stencils.

LAMPBLACK: One of the main ingredients of black printing inks.

LAYOUT: Preliminary sketch or arrangement showing size, and position of various elements used in printing a job.

LEAD: Strip of metal two points thick used for spacing between lines of type.

LEAD CUTTER: Small machine used to cut leads, slugs and rules.

LEADER: A row of dots or dashes.

LEDGER PAPER: A strong, smooth writing paper used for records and ledgers.

LENS: A piece of glass or a series of glass elements arranged to focus rays of light.

LETTERPRESS PRINTING: Printing from type or other raised surface.

LIGATURE: A type character on which two or more letters are cast on a single body.

LINE COPY: Copy suitable for reproduction without a halftone screen. The image will be printed as a solid color.

LINE ENGRAVING: Etched printing cut or plate containing solid lines and areas.

LINOTYPE: Trade name of a machine invented by Ottmar Mergenthaler in 1886, which assembles matrices from which are cast slugs or lines of type that may be used for printing.

LITHOGRAPHY: Type of printing based on principle that oil and water will not mix.

LIVE MATTER: Type matter to be used for printing.

LOCKUP: Process of locking type found in chase.

LUDLOW: A machine for casting lines of type from hand set matrices.

MACHINE COMPOSITION: Composition produced on typesetting machines.

MAKE-READY: Preparation of press to obtain proper printing impression.

MAKE UP· Arranging composed type into pages, columns, etc. for printing.

MATRIX: A brass mold used in casting letters on a typesetting machine such as a Linotype.

MITER: To cut rules or borders at an angle so they will fit properly at corners.

MONOTYPE: Typesetting machine which sets lines of individual letters.

NEGATIVE: In photography, a photographic image with lights and shades in reverse to those of the original subject.

NEWS INK: Ink used on an absorbent stock.

NICKELTYPE: A printing plate made in the same manner as an electrotype, except that nickel instead of copper is used in the first deposit in the mold.

NICK: A groove in the shank of a type character to enable the compositor to distinguish between different fonts of type when distributing, and to indicate, both by sight and touch, which is the bottom of a letter.

OFFSET: Transfer of ink from freshly printed sheet to back of another sheet. Also, a form of lithographic printing.

OLD STYLE: A style of letter in which mechanically perfect lines are not attempted, and there is but slight contrast between the light and heavy elements.

OPAQUE: Lithography - Water-soluble solution used to cover holes or block out undesirable portions of a negative.

OVERLAY: A piece of paper or other material pasted on tympan sheet of a printing press to equalize the impression.

OXIDATION: Drying of inks by contact with air, usually necessary when printed on hard-surfaced paper.

OZALID PRINT: A print made on ozalid paper which is printed by contact, but does not reverse the image. In other words, it prints a negative from a negative, and a positive from a positive.

PATENT BASE: A term applied to metal bases for printing plates.

PERFORATING: Making continuous series of holes or slits in paper so it will tear easily.

PHOTO-COMPOSITION: A method of composing reading matter by photographic methods instead of type.

PHOTO-ENGRAVING: Printing cut or plate, in which printing surface is in relief, made by photomechanical process.

PHOTOLITHOGRAPHY: The process of producing a lithographic picture or copy from a design made on plate photographically instead of by hand drawing or transfer.

pH VALUE: The degree of acidity or alkalinity measured on a scale from 0 to 14, with 7 as the neutral point.

PICA: A unit of type measurement equal to 12 points or 1/6 inch.

PIGMENT: The coloring matter in printing ink.

PLATEN PRESS: A printing press in which the impression is made when a flat surface called a platen pushes the paper against the type.

PLANOGRAPHY: Process of printing from a flat surface, based on inability of water-wet surface to take ink.

POINT SYSTEM: Printer's system of measurement. 1/72 in., 12 points equal one pica.

POSITIVE: Photographic image which shows lights and shades the same as the original subject.

PROCESS COLOR INK: Special inks used in process color printing, consisting of the three primary colors, yellow, red and blue.

PROOF: A trial printing impression used for examination and correcting of errors.

PUBLISH: To print and to offer for sale and general distribution, or to cause to be printed and distributed, a newspaper, book, magazine, pamphlet, piece of music, engraving, or the like.

PULP: The wood or other vegetable fiber from which paper is made.

QUAD: Piece of metal less than type-high used for spacing material in setting type.

RAG CONTENT PAPER: Paper made from material in which there is some quantity of rag.

REAM: A unit of quantity in paper, usually 500 sheets.

REDUCER: Any liquid or paste used to mix with printing inks to lessen their stickiness or adhesiveness.

REGISTER: Agreement in location of successively printed images.

RELIEF PRINTING: Printing from characters or designs that are raised above the surrounding surface.

REPRODUCTION RATIO: Term used to denote amount of enlargement or reduction when scaling copy.

REVERSE LETTERING: White lettering on a printed or dark background.

ROTARY PRESS: A printing press that uses curved printing plates and curved impression cylinder.

ROTOGRAVURE: A mass production method of gravure printing using a rotary press.

ROUTER: A machine used for the purpose of cutting away or cutting deeper parts in a printing plate.

RUN: Number of sheets to be printed.

SEPIA PRINT: Photo print in which portion that would ordinarily be black, is treated to give it a brown, or sepia color.

SERIF: Fine lines or cross strokes found at the tops and bottoms of Roman type faces.

SHOULDER: That part of the top of a type which is not covered by the letter.

SIGNATURE: A folded section of a book.

SIZED PAPER: Paper coated to seal the pores.

SLUG: Strip of type metal used for spacing between lines of type.

SLUG CASTING MACHINE: A typesetting machine which sets a complete line of type in one piece or slug, as distinguished from a machine which sets single letters.

SMASH: In bookbinding, to compress the folded signatures of a book together in order to take the swell out of the back of the book, so that it will be of even thickness and can be squarely trimmed and fitted into the cover.

SOLID MATTER: Type matter without leads or slugs between the lines.

SPACEBAND: On a typesetting machine, a device to place between words to press them apart and space them evenly.

SQUEEGEE: Device with rubber blade used to force ink or paint through silk screen.

STAMP: To impress or imprint with some mark or design, by pressure, and also the instrument with which the impression is made.

STAPLE: To fasten together the sheets of a book or pamphlet by means of wire staples; to stitch with wire staples.

STEREOTYPE: A duplicate printing plate or type form cast from a paper matrix.

STONE: Work table used in letterpress printing. Top surface is usually stone or steel.

STRAIGHT MATTER: Type composition set in plain, ordinary paragraph form.

SULPHITE PULP: A wood pulp produced by the sulphate process, used in making paper.

THERMOGRAPHY: Method of raising printed impression by heating special powder sprinkled over impression while it is wet.

TINT: A reduction of a solid color. Color made lighter by adding white.

TIP-ON: A sheet printed separately and glued to another sheet.

TRADE SHOP: An establishment which does work for those engaged in the same general line of trade or business, not for the general public.

TRANSPARENCY: A transparent positive photograph.

TRIM: To cut the edges of paper, books, etc., also, that part of the paper which is cut away.

TYMPAN: Sheets of paper or other material placed between the impression surface of a printing press, and the paper which is to be printed.

TYPE METAL: Combination of metals such as lead, tin and antimony used in the casting of type.

TYPE HIGH: Being of the exact height of type, or 0.918 in.

TYPOGRAPHY: The art of printing with type or of expressing by skillful use of type.

UNDERLAY: A piece of paper, cardboard, or the like, placed under type matter, plates, etc.; on the press, to bring it to the proper height for printing and to equalize the impression.

UNION LABEL: A trademark or label attached or printed on goods which have been produced by union labor. You will note this book bears a union label.

UPPER CASE: The name applied to the capital letters of the alphabet.

VAN DYKE PRINT: A silver print, or photographic image made on inexpensive paper.

VEHICLE: The carrier used in ink for transferring the pigment to the paper.

VIBRATING ROLLER: An inking roller on a printing press which distributes ink on other rollers, or on a table, by moving them back and forth endways in addition to its regular rotary movement.

VIGNETTE: A halftone or other engraving whose lines gradually fade away into the surrounding ground or the unprinted portion of the paper.

VISCOSITY: Resistance to flow.

WARM COLORS: Colors on the red side of the spectrum.

WATERMARK: A mark or design produced in some kinds of papers by pressure of the dandy roll in the wet paper during its progress through the paper-making machine.

WITH THE GRAIN: Parallel to or with the direction in which the fibers run in a sheet of paper or cardboard.

WOOD ENGRAVING: Process of cutting designs upon a block of wood, leaving the design in relief for printing.

WOOD PULP: Pulp made from wood and used in the making of paper.

WORK AND TURN LAYOUT: A single form which contains material that is to be printed on both sides of sheet. Entire form prints on one side of sheet for half the number of impressions, then the sheet is turned sideways from left to right and the run is completed on the reverse side of the sheet.

WORK-UP: A spot or mark on printed matter, caused by spacing material in a form working up during the press run and printing with the other matter.

WRONG FONT: Type of wrong type face.

XEROGRAPHY: A dry printing process by the electrostatic method.

XYLOGRAPHY: The art or process of engraving on wood, or of taking impressions from wood engravings.

ZINC ETCHING: Line engraving produced on zinc.

Acknowledgments

The author wishes to express here, his sincere appreciation to the many individuals and organizations whose co-operation has made this book possible. Special credit is due:

Advance Process Supply Co., Carpenter Paper Co., Challenge Machinery Co., Champlain Co., Inc., Chandler & Price Co., Craftsman Line-up Table Corp., John F. Cuneo Co., Davidson Corp., Denver Post, E. I. DuPont DeNemours & Co., Friden, Inc., Greeley Tribune, Hamilton Manufacturing Co., Hammermill Paper Co., Harris-Intertype Co., H. B. Rouse & Co., Heidelberg Pacific, Inc., Imperial Type Metal Co., Kimberly-Clark Corp., Lew Wenzel & Co., Ludlow Typographic Co., Mergenthaler Linotype Co., Miehle-Goss-Dexter, Inc., Minnesota Mining & Manufacturing Co., Robertson Photo-Mechanix, Inc., Rocky Mountain Club of Printing House Craftsmen, Vari-Typer Corp., West Virginia Pulp & Paper Co., James White Paper Co.

AUTOMATION AND
TECHNOLOGICAL CHANGE

Unit 15

All processes in the graphic arts are being changed by new automated machines and technological changes, but the composing room seems to be affected most.

The computer, which is changing many manufacturing processes, has also, some graphic arts applications. An example of a composing room taking advantage of these innovations is shown in Fig. 15-1.

Fig. 15-1. Harris-Intertype's composing room.

The reading machine at the left of the photo recognizes typewritten characters and translates them into punched tape codes. The tape is then processed by the computer, shown in the left rear. A justified tape provided by the computer is then used in the high-speed Intertype Fototronic printout unit shown at the right, rear. The machine may also be operated by tape from the keyboard console shown in the foreground. The keyboard has a built-in digital computer.

Another computer operating composing machine is shown in Fig. 15-2. This combination of machines will make up pages at the rate of 1000 characters per second. Text data are stored on magnetic tape, and illustrations on video tape. At the rate of about 10 pages per minute, halftones and

type will be assembled ready for the plate-making process.

The process camera is also being automated. One camera company makes a camera that is almost entirely operated from a control panel. It includes vacuum back loading, contact screen positioning, film loading and film discharging. While these operations are taking place, the camera operator loads and unloads copy.

Fig. 15-2. Mergenthaler's Lexical-Graphical Composer Printer System.

In directory, catalog and work of this nature, where lists of items or names need to be printed in order or sequence, Sequential Card Cameras speed up production. Cards containing information are printed or typed and kept in order in a file. When new editions of the listed material are needed, the cards are fed into this machine at speeds of 3600 to 7200 cards per hour. The card camera photo-

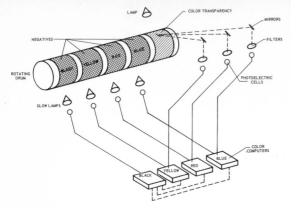

Fig. 15-3. Schematic diagram of the PDI Color Scanner.

graphs the cards as they pass through the machine, spaces the items, and produces a negative for making a printing plate. The cards can be punched and sorted by one of the electronic sorting systems. Trade names of some of the sequential card cameras are Listomatic, Fotolist, Compos-o-line.

In the field of letterpress plate making, special electronic engraving machines are being used to make halftones on metal and plastic plates. These machines pick up the tonal values of the photograph and through electronic circuitry convey the information to a stylus that cuts the plate to form

a halftone for printing. Several machines are available.

Color separation work can be produced from color transparencies without cameras. Starting with a color transparency mounted on a rotating cylinder, a beam of light is directed through the transparency. A mirror picks up the transmitted light and reflects it to other mirrors which filter the light for the primary colors. Photo-electric cells pick up the filtered light and send it through computers. The computers in turn send out color-corrected impulses to glow lamps that record the color on negatives for each of the colors. Each color computer sends proportionate impulses to a computer which in turn produces the black printer. The schematic diagram, Fig. 15-3, shows the operation.

Many other automated devices are reaching the market to help the graphic arts industry keep up with the technological revolution.

For Your Further Study

Arnold, E. C., INK ON PAPER, Harper and Row.

Auble, J. W., ARITHMETIC FOR PRINTERS, Chas. A. Bennett.

Carlsen, D. E., GRAPHIC ARTS, Chas. A. Bennett.

Clark, M. A., APPLIED COURSE FOR STUDENT PRINTERS, Chas. A. Bennett.

Cleeton, Pitkin, and Cornwell, GENERAL PRINTING, McKnight & McKnight.

Cogoli, J. E., PHOTO-OFFSET FUNDAMENTALS, McKnight & McKnight.

Eisenberg, J., Kafka, F. J., SILK SCREEN PRINTING, McKnight & McKnight.

Hague, C. W., PRINTING AND ALLIED GRAPHIC ARTS, Bruce.

Heller, J., PRINTMAKING TODAY, Henry Holt.

Jackson, H. E., PRINTING, PRACTICAL INTRODUCTION TO GRAPHIC ARTS, McGraw-Hill.

Kafka, F. J., LINOLEUM BLOCK PRINTING, McKnight & McKnight.

Karch, R. R., GRAPHIC ARTS PROCEDURES, American Tech.

Karch, R. R., HOW TO RECOGNIZE TYPE FACES, McKnight & McKnight.

Karch. R. R., PRINTING AND THE ALLIED TRADES, Pitman.

Kauffmann, D., GRAPHIC ARTS CRAFTS, D. Van Nostrand.

Lush, C. K., JUNIOR LETTERPRESS AND LITHOGRAPHY, Chas. A. Bennet.

Marinaccio, A., EXPLORING THE GRAPHIC ARTS, D. Van Nostrand.

McCombs, K. M., COMMERCIAL PHOTOGRAPHY, American Tech.

Miller, T. H., & Brummitt, W., THIS IS PHOTOGRAPHY, Garden City.

Ogg, O., THE 26 LETTERS, Thomas Y. Crowell.

Polk, R. W., and Polk, E. THE PRACTICE OF PRINTING, Chas. A. Bennett.

Pollack, P., PRINTING: CAREERS & OPPORTUNITIES FOR YOU, Chilton Co.

Turnbull, A. T., and Baird, R. N., GRAPHICS OF COMMUNICATION, Holt, Rinehart & Winston.

Superintendent of Documents, U. S. Gov. Printing Office, Washington, D. C., LITHOGRAPHER, 3 & 2, BUREAU OF NAVAL PERSONNEL.

OCCUPATIONAL OUTLOOK HANDBOOK, BUREAU OF LABOR STATISTICS.

PRINTER, 3 & 2, BUREAU OF NAVAL PERSONNEL.

INDEX